8/6.

SIXTY CENTURIES OF HEALTH AND PHYSICK

Nature e .7 f. melior er eo coctu mudu moderate coctuir . uuiame Iu
abit subauar mudificat 7 apetu . nocamieni chortu tussi 7 desuito
ne . remoto nocamien cu ulceb.

SIXTY CENTURIES OF HEALTH AND PHYSICK

THE PROGRESS OF IDEAS
FROM PRIMITIVE MAGIC
TO MODERN MEDICINE

BY

S. G. BLAXLAND STUBBS

AND

E. W. BLIGH

WITH AN INTRODUCTION BY

SIR HUMPHRY ROLLESTON, BART.
G.C.V.O., K.C.B., M.D., HON. D.C.L., LL.D., D.SC.

Regius Professor of Physic in the University of Cambridge,
Physician-in-Ordinary to H.M. The King,
Sometime President of the Royal College of Physicians.

Where there is love of man, there is also love of The Art.
(HIPPOCRATES.)

LONDON
SAMPSON LOW, MARSTON & CO., LTD.

To
H.C.M.
AND
H.E.P.

MADE AND PRINTED IN GREAT BRITAIN BY PURNELL AND SONS
PAULTON (SOMERSET) AND LONDON

INTRODUCTION

BY

SIR HUMPHRY ROLLESTON, BART.

G.C.V.O., K.C.B., M.D., HON. D.C.L., LL.D., D.SC.

Regius Professor of Physic in the University of Cambridge
Physician-in-Ordinary to H.M. The King
Sometime President of the Royal College of Physicians.

THE lay attitude to things medical has changed since the Victorian era; in the last century, in spite of the Scottish proverb that "every man at forty is a fool or physician," there was but little general interest manifested in Medicine and its progress, apart from the individual's anxiety about the ills of his own flesh. What Sir Andrew Clark (1826–93), a prominent London consulting physician, called "the laws of physiological righteousness," were then regarded as something quite unsuitable for ears polite, and conversation on physical disorders was so nearly taboo as to be in no way comparable with that on political, theological, or meteorological disturbances. Now that the ideal of Medicine is recognised to be the prevention of disease, it has become obvious that some knowledge of the laws of health is essential, and that the lay public should be educated in physical as well as in moral and religious well-being. Simple hygiene is now taught in all the State Schools, there are numerous voluntary societies actively engaged in improving the common health, and the Press, which reflects as well as directs public opinion, plays an important part in health propaganda. As Sir George Newman, the Principal Medical Officer of the Ministry of Health and of the Board of Education, said in his address, "Everyman in Preventive Medicine," at the Jubilee Congress of the Royal Sanitary Institute in 1926, "there is no public duty of more consequence than the education of the English people in health of body and mind," and it is a true saying that "the survival of the community is primarily dependent upon physical conditions— the life, health and capacity of the human body." Religion and Medicine—the care of the soul and of the body—were in ancient times combined so that the Medicine was in the hands

v

of the priesthood, and, though a cleavage took place, the Church-men preserved their prominent position. Medicine then became allied to science, and, as it shed the trammels of authority and tradition, became more and more an applied science, and has benefited from the enormous advances in science. Formerly, when the curative aspects of Medicine held the field, a little knowledge of Medicine was regarded as, at its best, but a doubtful acquisition, because it might encourage self-treatment and irresponsible drugging. But now, with the realisation of the importance of Preventive Medicine, this argument loses much of its force, and it is perhaps unnecessary to insist at greater length that there is now a growing general interest in the progress of Medicine. That this is desirable in the interests both of the individual and of the national well-being was clearly set out twenty-three centuries ago in Hippocrates' words, "Where there is love for humanity, there also is love for the art" of Medicine. The history of Medicine, and of the natural sciences which are so closely related, is indeed part of history as a whole.

In order to understand properly a man, an art, or a science, a knowledge of their development and past history is essential; what embryology is to the study of man's structure and evolution, history is to the comprehension of an art or a science. It is therefore reasonable that the study of the history of Medicine should have recently attracted increasing attention both in and outside the ranks of the profession. The progress of the science and art of Medicine, for in its different aspects Medicine is both of these, has not been constantly steady; the peaks of medical advance stand out against periods of quiescence and, as in the Dark Ages, even of deterioration. These advances have so often been due to the achievement of great pioneers that it is difficult to separate from the account of the development of the ideas, which is the real function of history, some reference to the personality of these responsible Masters of Medicine. It is, indeed, very tempting to branch off from philosophic ideas to the interesting biographies and the influence leading up to the activities of men such as Hippocrates, Galen, William Harvey, Sydenham, John Hunter, Edward Jenner, Laennec, Claude Bernard, Pasteur, Lister, and Patrick Manson. This difficulty, which increases as the story becomes more modern, is fully acknowledged by the authors of this attractive *Sixty Centuries of Health and Physick*, who accordingly have steered a wise course.

By the use of the old-fashioned word "physick" in the title, the evolution of surgery, obstetrics, and gynæcology has been eliminated from consideration, and attention has been concentrated on what in some countries is often called "internal medicine," to which the physician or "internist" devotes his activities.   This course fits in with the scope of the volume, which does not profess to be a complete history of Medicine. But the conventional distinction between "physick" and surgery, of which gynæcology is now a special branch, is fundamentally artificial, for it is not based on any difference in the science of disease, and indeed depends entirely on the form of treatment employed; this may vary from time to time; for example, much that was once within the provinces of the physician, such as intracranial or abdominal tumours, is now rightly excised by the knife; further, some superficial growths usually removed by the surgeon now melt away by radium or X-ray treatment, a method not yet designated either as surgical or medical. In tracing the evolution of "physick" from primitive magic to modern medicine the authors have successfully brought out the importance of the preventive idea which should permeate the teaching, practice, and research of the Medicine of the future.

PREFACE

IN THESE pages we are to follow in outline the evolution of ideas in the long quest for health from the earliest evidences of disease to the modern expansion of scientific medicine. Always it is the progress of ideas (and medical ideas, not surgical) and not a collection of historical incidents, with which we are to be concerned.

So we shall follow the dim traces of medical and hygienic ideas among primitive men, see their gradual slow emergence from the cast and matrix of magic and superstition in the earliest civilizations, herald the appearance of true hygiene in the marvellous sixty-century old Sumerian culture, and consider the remarkable mixture of commonsense and magic in Assyrian and Egyptian therapy. Then we hail the flowering of sane medical practice among the masters of art and science—the Greeks—paying due and wondering reverence to the great Master, Hippocrates. The Roman world produces no new ideas but keeps the Greek in bond, and is content to organize triumphantly, so that we see general medical services and military hospitals on a material scale.

Then the darkness descends, and all knowledge and science of four millennia are lost. Europe welters for a thousand years in gross magic and superstition until, with the first stirrings of re-birth of humanism, the Arabs are found to have preserved something of the "true faith" of medicine, and with the Renaissance medical science lifts up her head again, somewhat dashed by the great plagues of the thirteenth to seventeenth centuries, the Black Death and other epidemics, those constant enemies, against which little availed.

The fifteenth and sixteenth centuries break away from precedent and see the spread of original ideas, while the seventeenth sees the conscious application of scientific methods, and, with the great Sydenham, Hippocrates returns and clinical medicine is refounded. The eighteenth goes yet farther and opens the modern epoch with the establishment of preventive medicine, definite pathology, public hygiene and public hospitals. Medicine and its allied sciences expand amazingly when we enter the Golden Age of the nineteenth century.

Our necessarily rapid survey ends with a note on the great conquests and greater hopes of medicine to-day.

Certain names must inevitably stand out in the course of our reading for they are the names of great men, but primarily we are concerned with ideas not names. As the conventional school history of earlier generations made itself dull, and in the result uninforming, by presenting a catalogue of king-names and left us unaware that the common people existed, so the history of any science or branch of knowledge loses reality if it is content to recite a merely chronological series of biographies of individual scientists.

Often the great man of a discovery or period of marked advance is he who puts the coping-stone on the building of others. The great discoverers themselves with few, if any, exceptions do not fail to acknowledge that without the work of their predecessors and the urge of the "spirit of the time" their achievements would not be possible.

In particular, the latter part of the work has been written on the avowed principle that it is impossible to present the seventeenth, eighteenth or nineteenth centuries in detail and yet retain the spirit of the age. A forest of names is no satisfactory substitute for the particular shaft of sunlight across the woodland ride. Reference to any of the great Histories of Medicine will leave the lay reader dizzy with the cumulative effect of names that have contributed to the progress of medicine but will mean nothing to him in memory. He will also constantly be tripped up by technical matters which it is neither possible nor particularly important for him to grasp.

The method followed in this work is to seize the prevalent ideas of each age of medicine with some notes on the public health, to present them with due regard to the colour of the age, and ruthlessly to ignore minor names. All life is founded on thought. It is greater than the thinker, because it spreads and fecundates the surrounding country. The group of thinkers departs. Their thought moulds progress.

Thus, though those familiar with the bypaths and remoter details of the long record of medicine will find many omissions in this volume, all that the writers have cared about is that the reader should put it down with a clear idea of the progress of medicine and some notions on that of hygiene. They have not hesitated, where necessary, even to forsake the path of medicine proper if to do so sheds a fresher light on the journey.

They have also considered it of value and assistance to the ordinary reader, unable or unlikely to consult original authorities or to wade through copious tomes in search of the significant, to give considerable but careful selections of the actual words of the greater figures of medical history. Moreover, the reader is thereby assisted in making his own valuation of those figures who, in this way, can be given life much warmer and closer than any description at second-hand can afford.

So the reader is not to expect a comprehensive study of the History of Medicine. That has already been provided in many learned volumes. Nor is he to expect anything but a medical and hygienic study. The other and perhaps more important aspects —anatomy, biology, physiology and surgery—will, it is hoped, be dealt with in a companion volume. While the authors do not pretend to appeal to the learned student and the medical historian, it is incumbent upon them to acknowledge their indebtedness to the researches and writings of the original workers and to point the way for those who wish to pursue wider and deeper studies.

Among the great debts which the authors have to acknowledge is the courtesy of Dr. R. Campbell Thompson, the Assyriologist, who has not only permitted one of us to draw largely on his great corpus, the *Assyrian Medical Texts*, which are accessible only with great difficulty to the layman, but has very kindly read and corrected the chapter on ancient Mesopotamian medical and hygienic ideas, and so given it an " imprimatur " of great authority. Mr. W. H. S. Jones, Litt. D., President and Classical Lecturer of St. Catharine's College, Cambridge, has most kindly and generously permitted the use of extracts from his translations of Hippocrates in the Loeb Classical Library, including the "Aphorisms," which were not published when the book was printed. Acknowledgment is also due to the very helpful courtesy of Mr. Warren R. Dawson, one of the principal authorities in this country on Egyptian medicine and medical papyri. No one who writes anything which touches on any branch of medical history can fail to be indebted to Dr. Charles Singer, the erudite Lecturer in the History of Medicine, in the University of London.

Similarly acknowledgment is due to Dr. E. T. Withington, author of that entirely original and pioneer work, *Medical History*, now almost unobtainable; and to Dr. Fielding

H. Garrison, author of the monumental *History of Medicine*.

The division of labour is a matter of relative unimportance to the reader, but we think it fit to put on record that the first name on the title page carries responsibility for all matter up to the end of the sixteenth century (Chapters I to X and XIX) the remainder lying with the bearer of the second name, whose thanks are due to the Very Revd. Canon G. R. J. Fletcher, M.R.C.S., for his most kindly help in making special journeys to Farm Street and the British Museum to obtain, during the author's absence from London, passages from Kircher; to Mr. Arnold M. Muirhead for his translation from Kircher; to Dr. John Farquhar Fulton for looking over the chapter on the Oxford Respirationists, and for many kindnesses; to Dr. Hubert J. Norman, whose wonderful library and whose friendly portals have constantly been open to him: for assisting him, if he may so put it in the good, the Saintsbury, sense, *libris non sine Libero*; to Professor Clifford Dobell, F.R.S., for two helpful letters; and to Mr. Adrian Bury, without whose encouragement he would hardly have taken up pen.

The thanks of both authors are due to their friend, Mr. H. E. Powell, Librarian of the Royal Society of Medicine, for much invaluable criticism. Acknowledgment for assistance in the provision of illustrations is due, among others, to Dr. Charles Singer, to the Editor of *The Universal History of the World*, to Mr. G. P. Forrester, Editor of *The Chemist and Druggist*, and to Mr. L. W. G. Malcolm, Curator of the Wellcome Historical Medical Museum.

Fetcham, and Midhurst, 1931.

CONTENTS

CONTENTS xiii

PLATE I

Skull Cap
from above

Java
Thigh Bone

Modern
Thigh Bone

Skull Cap
from side

Molar Tooth

PLATE II

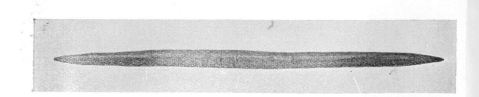

SIXTY CENTURIES OF HEALTH AND PHYSICK

CHAPTER I

PRIMITIVE NOTIONS OF HEALTH AND DISEASE

THAT THE intelligent man desires health above all boons is a platitude and a fundamental truth. The fact that health is to be sought for implies the fact of disease. The romanticists of the Rousseau school have postulated a Golden Age and a Noble Savage before civilization had laid its sophisticating and destroying fingers on Nature, healthy, happy and effortlessly wise. Science coldly brushes aside this figment and announces that germs, which we associate with disease, are as old as earthly life itself, and that bacteria and perhaps bacterial disease can be traced back to the Carboniferous Period, when the coal measures of central and northern England were laid down, some 160,000,000 years ago according to geological and physical calculations.

This figure is necessarily an approximate estimate, since though the physicists have, on radioactive data, assigned a total age for the Earth of between 1,500,000,000 and 2,000,000,000 years the geologists and the palæontologists are not agreed upon the time duration of the various Eras. The geologists are in general agreement as to the relative duration of Eras and Periods, but they are content, for lack of a geological time scale, to leave the time allotment to the physicists. Other scientists, including many zoologists, are unable to accept the length of period required by physical considerations. On the physical bases, for instance, the Tertiary or Era of Recent Life, has been allotted some 30,000,000 years while the zoologists are only prepared to give it 2,000,000—a discrepancy, large as it is, that is not unreasonable in the present state of knowledge. On this basis Sir Arthur Keith refers the most ancient remains of man to only about 350,000 years B.C.   This may be regarded as a minimum.   Others place them about 3,000,000 or more. In any event disease is far older than man, while the quest for health is obviously far younger.

Nevertheless, there is no evidence to show that disease was a factor of real importance before man appeared.   A few isolated cases have survived.   A number of fossil bones of extinct animals are found to show signs of disease (apart from injuries), as in the case of the dinosaur with a bone tumour, said to be the earliest known example of this disease.   A still earlier reptile of the Permian Period fractured a dorsal spine, which became infected and developed a chronic inflammation of a kind known to-day as osteo-myelitis.   According to Professor Roy Moodie this is not only the oldest example of this condition, but is the oldest vertebrate fossil known which shows the results of infection.   This carries disease in a form known to and still suffered by human beings back to some 130,000,000 years ago on the physical basis of computation or, say, 8,000,000 on the zoological basis.

A theory which held the field for some time assigned the apparently sudden disappearance of the race of enormous reptiles called dinosaurs to epidemic disease, but, while this is a possible cause, there is a lack of geological evidence either in support or in opposition.   Many of the modern epidemic diseases, with high mortality rates, leave no traces in the bones, and the dinosaur race may perhaps have been extinguished by such a disease.   In this same dinosaur period, however, we do find evidence of infective processes such as rheumatoid changes, osteitis (jaw bone inflammation) and dental decay.   A 40-foot dinosaur with jaws nearly three feet long suffering from toothache offers obvious possibilities to the comic artist.

These and other pathological conditions in pre-anthropoid fossil remains were of course due to bacterial infections and it is an astonishing fact that the minute forms of protoplasm called bacteria have been preserved in fossil specimens over an almost incredible number of millions of years.   The researches of M. Bernard Renault have proved the presence beyond doubt of bacteria of the micrococcus and diplococcus types in various forms of coal, in the fossilized fæces of fish and in vertebrate remains, all of the Carboniferous Period.   How they were preserved remains a palæontological puzzle.

When we come to the question of disease in prehistoric man and, what is more important to our inquiry, its treatment, we are still on difficult ground. The pathological evidence is similar to that which we have discussed above, and as scanty, since it is equally limited to bone changes.

On the medical side there has been much argument and theorizing from what the attorney called "the nature of the case" and from the promising though somewhat dangerous parallels supplied by modern primitives. A race like the aborigines of Central and North-western Australia is found to be using flint tools and weapons, and is dubbed Stone Age; but although it is an accepted principle, in any investigation, to argue from the known to the unknown, it does not necessarily follow, when the two are separated by many millions of years, that the later known supplies reliable evidence of the much earlier unknown. Although we shall consider the possibilities of elementary medical knowledge acquired by prehistoric man by perhaps painful experience, and although it will also be fitting in this chapter to note one or two outstanding examples of medical and hygienic practice among modern primitives, it is desirable to emphasize that knowledge of actual prehistoric medicine is practically non-existent.

To take the geological evidence first. Every textbook of palæontology dilates on the skill of prehistoric man in various forms of surgery, particularly trephining of the skull, which was widely performed in Neolithic times. Surgical matters, however, are outside our scope in this work, and we proceed to consider the human fossil remains which show signs of disease.

The first is the first creature with human characteristics which has so far been found. Pithecanthropus, the Java ape-man, whose skull, three teeth and one thigh bone were discovered in 1891, suffered from exostoses or bony outgrowths of his thigh bone, which made a tumour so large as to have inconvenienced him considerably [Plate 1]. Pithecanthropus belonged to the Pliocene Period and, according to Sir Arthur Keith's dating, is about 350,000 years old (i.e. the first certain human type). Such outgrowths of bone are not uncommon to-day, an interesting example being the rider's bone sometimes developed by men who spend much time in the saddle. It is a little ironic that even the earliest man known should not be without disease.

In the late Stone Age (Palæolithic) and Neolithic races we find many cases of fracture and diseased conditions following injury. Spondylitis deformans, a diseased and painful stiffening of the spinal joints and a progressive deformity, has frequently been found. A Neolithic grave, near Heidelberg, produced a skeleton showing the oldest case of Pott's disease, i.e., tuberculosis of the spine. Curvature of the spine, skull ulceration and many varieties of arthritic afflictions have also been found. The great pathologist Virchow investigated and described a number of instances of arthritis in Glacial times.

Though dental caries (decay of the teeth) has been considered to be a purely modern disease, and certainly was not common in men of the Stone Ages, yet examples do occur, as in the Neanderthal jaw found at Krapina, which showed clear signs of caries and tartar with arthritis deformans in addition. Rhodesian man (who represents, according to Keith, the stem from which both Australoid and Negroid man afterwards developed) suffered severely from caries and dental abscess. The skeletal remains found at Broken Hill showed ten teeth which were decayed and, significantly enough, rheumatoid changes in the left knee.

There is no room for doubt that caries is essentially a modern disease associated with modern soft foods which have altered and constricted nasal passages, jaw and palate shapes. As Sir Arthur Keith points out, in modern man 'there is a tendency to crowding and irregularities of the teeth; the palate and jaws do not grow and expand sufficiently . . . to give room for a symmetrical eruption of the teeth. . . . The teeth are not worn down [by coarse foods and bone-gnawing] as in Neolithic men. . . . The front teeth . . . do not meet edge to edge as in primitive races. . . . In the Neolithic people all these modern characters are absent. Abscesses or gumboils at the roots of the deeply ground teeth, however, were common; but there is not a single carious tooth to be seen in the Coldrum collection' [of Neolithic bones]. The wild chimpanzee is but slightly subject to this affliction, and the Australian aborigines almost entirely free, although they appear to succumb to it when they adopt the white man's diet.

Although he escaped most, if not all, of the modern dietary diseases it is clear that prehistoric man was faced with a variety of diseases, and it is hardly possible to suppose that individuals made no attempt to deal with these conditions. An animal when it is sick goes away by itself and waits for nature or death to relieve its distress. But if early man developed the intelligence necessary to fashion his really remarkable flint tools and weapons it is not unreasonable to argue that he would devise or discover some therapeutical methods of dealing with sickness, as we know he did in surgical conditions. Necessarily direct evidence is lacking, but a cautious application of parallels supplied by modern primitives may indicate possibilities worthy of consideration.

First comes the most obvious form—treatment by faith healing, generally considered by anthropologist or tribesman as magical or magico-religious, that is, some supernormal power as distinct from sorcery. When man began to think more or less consciously he would, as do the modern primitives, put on one side and label as magical or divine all the phenomena which he neither understood nor connected with simple causes.

The display of natural forces, such as thunder, storm winds and waterfalls, are obvious examples where the inherent magic is mixed with or even superseded by a religious element. In fact, Dr. Rivers was of opinion that the religious element in medical rites and leechcraft in all times has been under-estimated. So also is Dr. Marett. Medicine-man and priest are mingled in many, if not most, native cults. So we get the priest-king and the long survival of healing powers resident in the royal person and touch. Where disease or injury is ascribed to magic it is often said among primitive peoples, particularly those of the Pacific Islands and the Australian continent, to be due to hostile magic, i.e. witchcraft exercised by human agency in the person of a sorcerer. In other peoples, as in the European medieval period, it is due to evil spirits whose name is veritably legion.

Magic as a positive method in attacking the difficulties of life is perhaps as old as the recognition of disease. The marvellous paintings in the caves of the Dordogne and Eastern and Northern Spain provide definite evidence that Aurignacian man, some ten or twelve thousand years ago, used magic in his hunting, and it is hardly possible to assume that the magic, which was so powerful in providing his daily food, would not also be effective in other directions. The extraordinarily high artistic level of these paintings in dark recesses of deep caves (some critics are of opinion that, as examples of animal life studies, later art has never surpassed them) indicates too keen an intelligence to support the idea of so restricted an outlook.

The Australian aborigines consider that all sickness and accidents, if not due to the individual's own fault, such as breaking rules of conduct or tabu, are caused by hostile magic. A man's enemy points a poison bone [Plate 2] or stick at him at a distance, and this bone is invisibly sent into him by magic. The medicine-man, who possesses magic healing crystals [Plate 3], cures knowledge wider. They knew, for instance, the position of the heart of the bison. Whether in caves, river terraces or the open grass-lands they formed definite communities and increased care of the sick and injured may be postulated. Professor Fleure has pointed out that Aurignacian infant skulls show a delay in the closing of the sutures which not only permitted increased brain growth by enlarging the skull capacity, but suggests something in the nature of child welfare, since the period of infancy must have been prolonged. They not only believed in magic for hunting purposes (as indicated earlier), but in personal magical powers, if the painting in the Trois Frères cave, at Ariège, of a man in composite animal disguise is correctly interpreted as representing a magician.

These food-gathering peoples necessarily had experience of all kinds of fruits, berries and edible grasses and plants, and though it is a matter of inference rather than precise evidence it seems indubitable that they discovered by painful experience that some berries and plants were not only unpleasant but poisonous. Professor G. Renard, in his *Life and Work in Pre-historic Times*, concludes that "in different countries and in different times man discovered tea, coffee, maté, cocoa and the kola nut, all plants which were used by uncivilized peoples before being adopted by the civilized. One must also mention the poppy from which opium comes, hemp which produced hashish, and coca which produces cocaine. Man seems to have discovered the properties of these very early, a knowledge which remained the property of priests, sorcerers and medicine-men."

With the return of the colder conditions referred to above, and the great climatic changes which followed the final retreat of the ice, European man gradually became more scattered and impoverished owing to the increasing reduction in natural food supplies. The hunting societies died out some time after 5000 B.C., and the centre of interest shifts to Egypt and the Near East.

From the brief study which we have made of early man we may credit him with a higher level of health than the products of most civilizations, although his ideas of medicine and health appear to be but a crude mixture of the animal and animistic.

PLATE III

PLATE IV

CHAPTER II

ACHIEVEMENTS AND SUPERSTITIONS OF SUMERIANS, BABYLONIANS AND ASSYRIANS

ONE OF the difficulties of a sketch of any section of civilization lies in the fact that the sequence of civilizations is not an ordered affair like a railway timetable. Civilization in Europe in the sense in which we know it was a much later affair than in the East. After the disappearance of the food-hunters various stages of culture developed in different areas at different times. Neolithic (New Stone), Chalcolithic (copper and stone) and Bronze and Iron Ages endured and were succeeded at unequal intervals, so that while some peoples were still using stone implements others were well advanced in the use of copper and its alloy, bronze. So the Bronze Age in Scandinavia is contemporary with the fully developed Iron Age in Central Europe. None of these cultures, interesting though they be, was so highly developed or so important in the history of civilization, or in the subjects of our study, as those of the Near East and Egypt. It is true that, as we have already mentioned, Neolithic peoples showed surprising skill in some forms of surgery. So also did the men of the Bronze Age, but in both cases we have no knowledge to lead us to suppose that their ideas of medicine and hygiene differed considerably from those of the primitive peoples of Palæolithic times.

So we leave these somewhat rude peoples of barbaric Europe who cover, generally, the period from about 7000 B.C. to 600 B.C., and turn to the Near East somewhere about the end of the fifth millenium B.C. about the time when, it will be remembered, the primitive food-hunting societies of Europe died out. The question may be asked—Why begin with the Near East instead of Egypt? It is certainly the fashion with the older schools of historical writers, and a dogma held almost passionately by one modern school of anthropologists, that first in time and first in importance was Egypt and that from Egypt came all. *Ex Aegypto lux*, to vary the tag. But the majority of scholars are unable to accept this diffusionist theory of culture and consider that

9

South-west Asia was the original home of civilization. We shall therefore discuss first the Near East—Mesopotamia, and its related cultures.

Mr. C. Leonard Woolley, the well-known excavator of the ziggurat and cities of Ur, considers that the objects he has uncovered in his diggings show that the Sumerian was not only a magnificent craftsman in metal when the pre-dynastic Egyptian was making fine flints, but indicate a craft tradition and an elaborate system of trade that must have had their roots in a period many hundreds of years earlier.

The Sumerians were established in Babylon some time after 5000 B.C. and already by this time, if not earlier, an ordered civilization had been achieved, for they organized a kingship with dynasties grading from traditional to actual at Erech, Ur, Kish, Lagash and other centres. The monarchical development may perhaps be gauged by the fact that, as Mr. Woolley has discovered in the great Death Pit at Ur, when the king (or other members of the royal household) died, his gaily clad retinue of nobles, ladies, servants and oxen accompanied him to the next world of which they obviously had a clear and certain idea.

That they accompanied him willingly and died peacefully is shown by the ordered arrangement of the bodies under the weight of the earth overlaid at the time of the burial. Mr. Woolley has expressed the opinion that this peaceful end was attained by the use of soporific drugs. If this were the case— and it is difficult to provide any other explanation of the facts—it would indicate medical knowledge of a kind whose limits it would be difficult to gauge when the extraordinarily high level of early Sumerian achievement in other directions is remembered.

Though they had no stone they could build great temples, beautifully decorated; they could lay out wide spreading cities; they provide what is considered by some experts to be the earliest evidence of agriculture in the growth of fine wheat; and their superb craftsmanship, many astonishing examples of which have been seen in the yearly exhibitions of objects obtained by the Joint Expedition of the University of Pennsylvania and the British Museum to Ur, could only be equalled by the most skilled of modern silver and goldsmiths.

These people and their predecessors in type had settled down in the delta land "of Sumer and Akkad", a land made by the silting up of the Tigris and Euphrates and a land so fertile that not

only does the date palm grow untended, but one that can bear
two or three crops of wheat in a year. What is known as the
Elamite culture had been developing here for an immensely long
period—possibly several thousand years—while the primitive
pastoral peoples on the desert margins had been profiting, as
Professor J. L. Myres puts it, "from their raids" on "the settlements on the opposite edges of the desert, and in particular by
their own knowledge and exploitation of desert herbs, many of
which are fragrant or medicinal, and consequently in great
request wherever their properties are known. Frankincense,
myrrh, balm of Gilead, ladanum and a score of others, chiefly
gums or resins exuded during the summer heat, are the stock-in-
trade of the desert herbalist."

It will be noted later that all these drugs and many more are
commonplaces in the medical texts from Ashurbanipal's great
library at Nineveh which undoubtedly repeat traditions and
practices of much earlier times. This knowledge must have
been at the disposal of the highly cultured men of Ur, Kish,
Ashur and Akkad and of their contemporaries or collaterals on
the Indus. The earliest Sumerian script, which comes from Kish,
is dated by Dr. Langdon to 4200 B.C., and is crudely picto-
graphic. Kish was, perhaps, the most ancient of Mesopotamian
cities of which record exists. It was the seat of a wealthy and
cultured dynasty, ruling Sumer and Akkad before the rise of
Ur. Here Dr. Langdon has found tablets bearing on medicine.
A physician's seal from Lagash is shown in Plate 8.

Of hygiene we have some definite and surprisingly early
evidence. In the Indus Valley and the Punjab Sir John Marshall's
excavations at Mohenjo Daro and Harappa have uncovered
brick-built cities, one of which, dating back to about 3500 B.C.,
displays hygienic ideas of an astonishingly high level. Not only
are there bath-rooms in the private houses with waterproofed
brick floors and house latrines [Plate 6], but a system of drainage
with socketed drain pipes was provided by which the sewage was
carried into street tanks, and thence removed by scavengers [Plate
5.] This civilization was at first called Indo-Sumerian because the
evidence obtained showed close relations with the Sumerians
of Mesopotamia. It may conceivably pre-date it.

At Kish, Dr. Langdon states, the Blundell-Field Expedition
found sanitary drains as early as 3000 B.C. By 2000 B.C. we find
tiled lavatories in the Sumerian courtyard and balcony houses
of Ur, and each house provided with drains and efficient soak-
aways.

The contrasts with Europe are heightened when we remember that at this time the Bronze Age peoples of England were living in small grass or mud-covered huts.

This is the time of Hammurabi, the great law-giver of Babylon, and we find him, in the epilogue to his Code (preserved on a diorite pillar in the Louvre), among his many boastings, recognizing the importance of the public health: "The righteous laws which Hammurabi the wise and perfect king established . . . by which he gave the land stable support and pure government . . . I expelled the enemy . . . I brought health to the land . . . I made the populace to rest in security . . . In my bosom I carried the people of the land of Sumer and Akkad."

Clearly then the ancient people of Mesopotamia lived an ordered, busy and reasonably hygienic life, from which we may deduce a common-sense knowledge of medicine and disease, although we have details only of the time of Hammurabi (c. 1950 B.C.) and later, and then, as earlier, thickly overlaid with what we regard as superstition and magic which survived from the traditions and practices of the primitive peoples described in the first chapter. We have but little reason, however, for dismissing Babylonian and Assyrian magic as pointless stupidities, for the European medieval period provides a large number of sufficiently chastening parallels. In fact, as Dr. C. H. W. Johns remarks in his *Babylonian and Assyrian Laws*, "the right thinking citizen of a modern city would probably feel more at home in ancient Babylon than in medieval Europe."

The great Code of Hammurabi is of particular interest in the history of medicine for two reasons. One is that it is a reversion to a much older Sumerian original of which fragments have been found and the other is that although the relevant clauses speak of a physician (*asu*) or healer, we find that, as Dr. Morris Jastrow has pointed out, the physician as surgeon was already to some extent "differentiated from the healer of diseases and perhaps not placed on the same level as the latter." Perhaps for this reason the Code applies the old primitive *lex talionis* to the unsuccessful operator as we see in the following clauses (the only clauses of medical interest in the Code):

215. If a physician operate on a man for a severe wound (or make a severe wound upon a man) with a bronze lancet and save the man's life; or if he open an abscess (in the eye) of a man with a bronze lancet and save that man's eye, he shall receive ten shekels of silver (as his fee).

216. If he be a free man, he shall receive five shekels.

PLATE V

PLATE VI

PLATE VI
Bathrooms and Drains in India and Mesopotamia between Four Thousand and Five Thousand Years Ago

The vertical pottery drain pipe from a house at Mohenjo-Daro (top left) with its elaborate brick covering, partly removed, and its efficient jointing betoken an exact hygienic knowledge such as, with the exception of Minoan Crete, we do not find again for nearly five thousand years.

The social condition, indicated by the paved bathroom and brick well from another house at Mohenjo-Daro, reached a very high level. Baths and latrines, with a public system of scavenging, were also discovered in the earliest of the three cities excavated, dating about 3300 B.C.

The perforated drain from Ur (top right) dates from about 2400 B.C. and had a partly sacrificial and partly hygienic use.

Sir John Marshall, Director-General of Archæology in India, and Mr. C. Leonard Woolley, Joint Expedition to Ur.

217. If it be a man's slave, the owner of the slave shall give two shekels of silver to the physician.

221. If a physician set a broken bone for a man or cure his diseased bowels, the patient shall give five shekels of silver to the physician.

222. If he be a free man, he shall give three shekels of silver.

223. If it be a man's slave, the owner of the slave shall give two shekels of silver to the physician.

We have here a very early example of the differentiation in payment by social status which obtains in the medical world to-day. Ten shekels would now be worth roughly £2.

It has to be noted that where the Code speaks of "a man" a person of the upper classes—a gentleman or nobleman—is indicated. The freeman is a plebeian who may own a certain amount of property or one or two slaves. The detailed regulation of the medical profession indicates that it was then highly organized.

That medical ideas and treatment, as well as those of surgery, were familiar is evident from the following paragraph in the Epilogue, the fifteenth and final of a series in which Hammurabi calls down elaborate curses on his successor "if he do not pay attention to my words . . . if he abolish the judgements I have formulated, overrule my words." The curses are called down from Bel, Shamash, Sin, Adad and the other Babylonian gods, and wind up:

> May Nin-kar-ra-ak, the daughter of Anu, who commands favours for me in E-kur, cause to come upon his members until it overcome his life, a grievous malady, an evil disease, a dangerous sore, which cannot be cured, which the physician cannot diagnose, which he cannot allay with bandages and which like the bite of death cannot be removed. May he lament the loss of his vigour!

We have now to jump an apparent interval of thirteen hundred years, but the interval is more apparent than real, for the great collection of seventh century texts we are to consider are, it appears, an inheritance. There are actually texts existing which are earlier in date. A few fragments in Semitic cuneiform characters from Boghaz Keui, the Hittite capital, date from about 1500 B.C. and are, according to Dr. Campbell Thompson, surprisingly like the seventh century texts. A number of the Assyrian texts from Ashur of the ninth to seventh centuries are also duplicates. The main collection is the work of the comparatively late reign of Ashurbanipal (668–626 B.C.) king of Assyria, the available seventy-five years after the discovery of the tablets themselves.

Translations published in various scientific journals between 1924 and 1931 include texts dealing with diseases of the head, diseases of the mouth and nose (including toothache and tooth troubles), the eyes, the ears, the stomach and digestive organs generally, and with ulcers, poisons, swellings or blows, the condition of the urine and also with childbirth.

The few examples of prescriptions and treatments which can be given here are chosen partly for their interest and partly for their completeness. Of the many hundreds translated the greater portion are fragmentary, due to the breaking of the clay tablets and do not lend themselves to quotation in a popular work.

A common theory of Babylonian medicine attributed disease to invisible demons entering the man's body. For "demon" read "microbe", and the theory becomes modern. The Babylonian physician, at times, called in the aid of magic to assist his often sensibly chosen medicines in routing the "demon", and to therapeutic "ritual" we have magic, incantation and charm added [see Plate 8].

Another theory made it the consequence of transgression of tabu and divine laws (as we noted with the Australian primitives, page 5). In the medical texts certain sicknesses are attributed to "the hand of Ishtar" or other god. Dr. Thompson has translated over ninety prescriptions for diseases brought about by the "hand of a ghost".

It must not be forgotten, however, that these medical tablets represent the armamentarium of the ancient Mesopotamian physicians, the knowledge and experience gained in centuries of daily practice, and they deserve not to be dismissed lightly. If some of the medicaments are foolish seeming, medicine sixteen hundred years later could equal them; if some are disgusting that is because magic declared they were necessary to disgust the "demon".

Often a genuine remedy is compounded with an unpleasant ingredient to disgust the demon. So turpentine is mixed with a green frog, sesame with doves' dung, cherry and antimony with a dried and powdered old shoe. Two closely associated examples in the section dealing with diseases of the eyes bring out these points.

If a man's eyes are affected with dryness he shall rub an onion, drink it in beer, apply oil to his eyes.

PLATE VII

A

B

C

PLATE VIII

PLATE VIII

SEAL OF A SUMERIAN PHYSICIAN, c. 3000 B.C.

The Babylonians signed their documents by rolling over the wet clay an engraved cylinder, such as this, belonging to a physician, from Lagash, and now in the Louvre. It represents Iru, a deity regarded as a form of Nergal, the god of pestilence and disease. The cuneiform characters are of an early type (cf. Plate VII).

From a cast in the Wellcome Historical Medical Museum.

ANCIENT MESOPOTAMIAN RELIGION AND DISEASE

Disease was largely of demon origin and consequently priests (left, from Nineveh, eighth century B.C.) could combat it. Demonic figures were set up at the gates or buried beneath house thresholds (right) to frighten demons away. The centre figure, in bronze, was buried beneath the floor of a room, and was supposed to be able to drive away the demons of sickness.

British Museum.

As Dr. Thompson remarks, drinking a raw onion would presumably induce tears. For the same or a similar condition the same tablet states:

> Thou shalt disembowel a yellow frog, mix its gall in curd, apply to his eyes.

Although frog gall appears merely nasty, it has, apparently, real value in some eye conditions. Reptile gall diluted was used by the Egyptians as a solvent for obscuring films on the eye, in which it has been shown to have a definite effect. Throughout the East eye troubles have, apparently, been common, as they are to-day, and this fact is demonstrated by the tablets.

Over one hundred and twenty treatments in addition to charms and incantations are indicated in Dr. Thompson's translations. A few may be quoted. First we have a case of inflammation with a film over the eyes, like that seen in acute conjunctivitis, coupled with pain if the eyes are used.

> If a man's eyes are sick and full of blood, unguents only irritating (?) the blood, blood and tears coming forth from the eyes, a film closing over the pupils of his eyes, tears turning to film, to look oppressing him: thou shalt beat leaves of nigella, "gum of copper", separately thou shalt bray: thou shalt take equal parts of them, put them together; pour them into the helmet in which thou hast squeezed the tamarisk; in curd and šuniš-mineral thou shalt kneed it, and open his eyes with a finger and put it in his eyes. While his eyes contain dimness, his eyes shalt thou smear, and for nine days thou shalt do this.
>
> *Charm.* O clear eye, O double clear eye, O eye of clear sight! O darkened eye, O doubly darkened eye, O eye of darkened sight! O eye of sleepy (?) sight, O eye of . . . sight, O eye of evil sight! O failing eyes, O painful eyes, . . . eyes, like the slaughter of a sheep . . . like hay (?) thrown away, like a cup of sour wine (vinegar) thrown away . . . of these twain Nergal between them a boundary hath set . . . The charm is not . . . (?): it is the charm of Ea and Marduk . . . the charm of Nin-aha-kuddu the mistress of charm; Gula quicken the recovery and take thy fee. Recite the charm.

The charm comes at the end of the tablet and is to be used with this and three other treatments. The next is a charm from a tablet [Plate 7, C] which consists entirely of charms and incantations and obviously refers to a very common cause of eye disease—dust-laden wind.

C

(?) poison his whole body; it hath seized neck (?), shins (?), hips, broad belly and shoulders. Marduk, who is glorious and wise, knoweth it all, too, and may the incantation which divideth all results (?) as between day and night, divide also between the sickness and his body.

Digestive troubles were serious. Tablet after tablet in the section dealing with stomach diseases begins: "If a man's stomach burns," or "If a man eats bread and drinks beer and his stomach is constricted." A somewhat heavy concoction of aromatics for heartburn is the following, a virtue of the prescription being the temporary prohibition of food:

> If a man has heartburn, and his stomach holds " fire " . . . his chest rending him, that man is suffering from the heat of the day . . . hellebore, lupins, calendula, chrysanthemum segetum, . . . gum of Andropogon (?), manna, ricinus (castor oil), lolium, . . . together thou shalt pound, in beer without a meal let him drink, and he shall recover.

Many prescriptions show that the Babylonian and Assyrian physicians were acquainted with methods of treatment in common use to-day. This, for instance, exhibits a perfectly correct opium suppository:

> If a man's belly unexpectedly is irritated, he holding wind in his anus, food and water being returned, and he being affected with constriction of the anus, and while it hurts him he cries out, and it is grievous upon him . . . thou shalt reduce lion-skin, mix with lion fat (opium): let it dry again, mix with cedar oil, make into a suppository, put it to his anus.

At one time the Egyptians were supposed to have discovered the use of the enema, but many enemas are prescribed in these tablets. Other non-drug treatments ordered in addition to those quoted above, are poultices (a large variety including linseed), bandages, plasters (including a mustard plaster for the back) compresses, salves, eye washes, unguents, liniments and aperients. As a final example we cannot do better than quote a marvellous 'cure-all' of the 'buckshot' variety which doctors more than two thousand years later were not ashamed to imitate:

> If a man's head hurts him, his mouth pricks him, his eyes trouble him, his ears sing, his throat chokes him, his neck muscles hurt him . . . his fundament, his breast, his shoulders and his loins hurt him, his fingers are cramped, his stomach is inflamed, his bowels are hot, . . . his hands, his feet and his knees ache, he

has . . . either his bowels are affected, or his kidneys are upset-
ting him . . . or he is sick of retention, either restriction of constipation or restriction of breath . . . or he is sick of nephritis (?)
or is sick of bile, or is sick of jaundice . . . of is sick from a
curse, or is sick of ulcers (?), or of rheumatism, or of the hand of
a ghost . . . or is sick of the demon " Raiser of the Head for
Evil " . . . To assuage his obsession . . . poppy, " stone " of
poppy (opium), Artemisia, balsam, Sagapenum, . . . licorice,
root of licorice, male Mandragora . . . kankadu, sumach,
lidrušu, Salicornia-alkali (glasswort), . . . fennel, fennel root,
saṣumtu, Arnoglosson (plantain) . . . Solanum.

To conclude on this note would leave a wrong and unfair
impression which must be corrected by noting the methods of
treatment shown in the letters of the royal physician as translated by Mr. Leroy Waterman in *Royal Correspondence of the
Assyrian Empire* (Michigan, 1930). Here we see evidence of
detailed diagnosis and care in observing symptoms. Arad-Nana,
the physician, writes to Esarhaddon (brother and predecessor of
Ashurbanipal) about a man in whom the king is interested:

ARAD-NANA TO KING ESARHADDON.

The king my lord your servant Arad-Nana. May it be sur-
passingly well with the king my lord. May Ninib and Gula grant
health of mind and body to the king my lord.
It is very well indeed with this unfortunate man whose eyes are
diseased. I had put a dressing on them to cover his face. Yesterday toward evening the bandage which held it on I removed. I
took off the dressing that was there. There was pus on it the size
of the tip of the little finger. Whoever of your gods has put his
hand to this case has himself surely given his orders (explicitly).
It is extremely well. May the heart of the king my lord be of good
cheer. In seven or eight days he will be well.

The same physician writes to the king concerning a boil or
eruption. A significant point is that the king is cautioned to
wash his hands thoroughly after he has put some ointment on
his face. May we perhaps see in this a vague recognition of the
possibility of transferring the infection from the boil on the chin
elsewhere?

As to the eruption (?) concerning which the king has made
inquiry . . . for the rest of the time he should take a complete
rest. Let the king apply to his chin. Let the king draw pure
water with which to thoroughly wash the hands of the king, my
lord. Do not worry. Soon the eruption will pass away.—(*Jastrow's
translation.*)

drew the proper conclusion and translated knowledge into action. Those affected with this disease must be debarred from intercourse with the healthy.   Whoever was defiled by *issubbu* was banished to the wilderness.—(*Sudhoff*.)

So with the ancient Hebrews. Leviticus lays down the strictest injunctions regarding unclean objects, proper foods, the hygiene of childbirth and menstruation and the prevention of contagion. Outstanding chapters are those which deal with the diagnosis and prevention of leprosy, gonorrhoea and leucorrhoea where the directions concerning segregation and disinfection—the very walls of the infected house are ordered to be scraped or the house destroyed—together with the incineration of the patient's clothes or objects he has used, are modern in their efficiency. They provided the model, which the Middle Ages adopted completely, for the treatment of lepers.

The Egyptians, whom we shall next consider, reached a definitely higher level than Babylonians or Assyrians in the true progress of medicine, particularly in the early days of the Old Kingdom. But even their progress is somewhat disappointingly limited.

PLATE IX

IMHOTEP, THE FIRST PHYSICIAN OF HISTORY

The first recorded physician, Imhotep, was vizier, architect and physician under Zoser, King of the 3rd Egyptian Dynasty (c. 2900 B.C.). He became a deity and is generally represented seated with a scroll.

British Museum; photo, Mansel.

PLATE IX

IMHOTEP, THE FIRST PHYSICIAN OF HISTORY

The first recorded physician, Imhotep, was vizier, architect and physician under Zoser, king of the 3rd Egyptian Dynasty (*c.* 2900 B.C.). He became a deity and is generally represented seated with a scroll.

British Museum ; photo, Mansell.

PLATE IX

[40660]

PLATE X

PLATE X

Pages from the Famous Ebers Medical Papyrus, c. 1550 b.c.

These three folios include eighteen prescriptions. The papyrus, which has not yet been adequately translated (see note on the difficulties of translation of Egyptian medical papyri on page 30), is written in hieratic script. It has claims to be considered the oldest medical book surviving. The contents of these folios, according to Dr. Georg Ebers, are as follows;

Left. Three recipes for treating diarrhœa, including grapes, honey, onions, figs, green lead (?) dough, flour, white of egg (?) The weights of the separate ingredients are given in left hand column since the hieratic script reads from right to left.

Centre. Four recipes for expelling worms. No. 1 (begins line 3) reads; "cyperus tuber 1/32, verdigris 1/32, water 1/3, boil and take four days." Between each recipe are repeated two signs which mean " another."

Right. This folio contains eleven recipes for diseases of the eyes, including a formula for verdigris ointment, also known as Egyptian ointment, which fills lines 2 to 6 (from top.) The ingredients are: Sa-seeds of Upper Egypt (saltpetre), red lead, verdigris, and honey, equal parts. This ointment is recommended in the treatment of conjunctival catarrh with swelling.

From Georg Ebers, " The Ebers Papyrus," 1875.

PLATE X

PAGES FROM THE FAMOUS EBERS MEDICAL PAPYRUS, c. 1550 B.C.

These three folios include eighteen prescriptions. The papyrus, which has not yet been adequately translated (see note on the difficulties of translation of Egyptian medical papyri on page 30), is written in hieratic script. It has claims to be considered the oldest medical book surviving. The contents of these folios, according to Dr. Georg Ebers, are as follows:

Left. Three recipes for treating diarrhoea, including grapes, honey, onions, figs, green lead (?) dough, flour, white of egg (?) The weights of the separate ingredients are given in left hand column since the hieratic script reads from right to left.

Centre. Four recipes for expelling worms. No. 1 (begins line 3) reads: "cyperus tuber 1/32, verdigris 1/32, water 1/3, boil and take four days." Between each recipe are repeated two signs which mean "another."

Right. This folio contains eleven recipes for diseases of the eyes, including a formula for verdigris ointment, also known as Egyptian ointment, which fills lines 2 to 6 (from top). The ingredients are sa-seeds of Upper Egypt (salpetre?), red lead, verdigris, and honey equal parts. This ointment is recommended in the treatment of conjunctival catarrh with swelling.

From Georg Ebers, "The Ebers Papyrus," 1875.

CHAPTER III

IN THE discussion of Egyptian medicine and hygiene some discrimination in respect of time is necessary. We are dealing here with a period exceeding three thousand years in the crowded history of a great people during which empires rise and fall and, towards the end, the Western world comes to that great fruition which we know as the civilizations of Greece and Rome. External contacts by commerce and conquest are many and far-reaching and some at least of the material achievements can only be described by that much over-worked word "stupendous". Yet relative to their other great achievements the Egyptian advance in the science of medicine, considerable though it is, does not appear to be really great. Its measure and the reasons for it will appear.

We shall not attempt to add colour to our subject by giving any sketch of Egyptian civilization, for that information is readily available in many popular forms. We need merely erect a slight chronological framework. The main divisions are:

(1) The pre-Dynastic period, covering Palæolithic, Neolithic, and Chalcolithic (copper and stone using) cultures up to 3400 B.C., when

(2) the Old Kingdom begins with the First Dynasty, includes the Great Pyramid Age (Fourth Dynasty 2900—2750 B.C.), and ends in anarchy in 2430 B.C.;

(3) the Middle Kingdom (2160–1788 B.C.) includes the Eleventh and Twelfth Dynasties, and then anarchy supervenes until

(4) the Eighteenth Dynasty establishes after 1580 B.C. the New Kingdom and the First Empire. This lasts for five hundred years until, a century after the fall of Troy, the death in 1094 B.C. of the last of the Rameses, a mere nonentity, sees its final disruption.

(5) The old order is now definitely at an end, various dynasties rise and fall, brief periods of power are experienced
with periods of conquest by Assyria and Persia until
Alexander's conquest in 332 B.C. For the next three hundred years the Ptolemies (among whom was Cleopatra)
rule and in 30 B.C. Egypt sinks to relative obscurity as a
province of Rome.

To the classical world Egyptian medicine, as other branches
of knowledge, stood as the archetype. For long centuries to be
"learned in the wisdom of the Egyptians meant the possession
of all knowledge."—(*Osler*.) Homer speaks of the high position
of Egyptian medicine. This evaluation, however, has to be
limited to the earlier times. In the Old and Middle Kingdoms
we have medical knowledge which has claims to scientific pretensions although the appearance of dung and other substances
in the therapeutics indicates the idea of driving out the demon
of disease which bulked so largely in Mesopotamian medicine.
In the New Kingdom, and later, magic and incantation reappear
and real progress is stopped.

As in Babylon, priest and physician are identical or closely
associated, and in fact Egyptian medicine never obtained complete divorce from religion. The Egyptian shared the belief of
all men in the early days (up to the days of the Greeks) and of
modern primitives that disease and death were not inevitable,
but due to a malign influence which could use any natural or
invisible agency. As Gaston Maspero, in his *Life in Ancient
Egypt*, puts it:

> Whoever treats a sick person has two equally important duties
> to perform. He must first discover the nature of the spirit in
> possession and, if necessary, its name and then attack it, drive it
> out. . . . He can only succeed by powerful magic, so he must
> be an expert in reciting incantations and skilful in making amulets.
> He must then use medicine (drugs and diet) to contend with the
> disorders which the presence of the strange being has produced in
> the body.

In early Egypt the physician was a man of honour, and the
earliest who appears in the records attained the rank of demi-
god. This was Imhotep, the chief minister, architect and
physician of Zoser (c. 2980 B.C.), whose terraced pyramid, 190
feet high, the first built in stone, was designed by Imhotep.
Perhaps the apotheosis of an actual personality, so great a reputation for wisdom in magic, medicine and architecture attached

to the name that it was never forgotten and as a god of medicine was identified by the Greeks with Asklepios [Plate 9].

A more definite personality emerges about two hundred and fifty years later in a physician to King Sahu-ra of the Fifth Dynasty, named N-enekh-Sekhmet, whose mastaba tomb at Sakkara records the royal gratitude for his healing of the king's nostril. His memorial stone carries a sculptured inscription describing him as "Pharaoh's physician" and shows him wearing the leopard skin, a garment usually reserved for priests of high rank.

The succeeding king of the same dynasty, Neferirika-ra (2730 B.C.), had a high priest named Ra-Ouer, who held the office of royal barber; two flint razors were found in his tomb, which was excavated by an expedition of the Egyptian University in 1930. The same expedition discovered another high priest's tomb, on a stele (tablet) in which were inscribed his titles and those of his father and mother. His mother was described as "Chief Physician." This is a matter of unusual interest, for she is the first woman of the Old Kingdom known to be so described, although it is known that both then and in the later Middle Kingdom women took very active and even commanding parts in the life of the community.

In the Berlin Museum there is preserved the travelling pharmacy of a queen of the Eleventh Dynasty, about 2970 B.C. It was a somewhat elaborate affair, consisting of a palm fibre case and stand, carried in a strong wooden box. The six compartments carried five alabaster vases and one serpentine vase, spoons, scoops and a faïence bowl. Root and other remains were found in the vases. It is not difficult to imagine that the queen carried and used the drugs for more than personal use. Was she, in other words, a "doctor" like the lady of the Fifth Dynasty? Mr. Warren Dawson is, however, of the opinion that the case was used for toilet purposes.

When we discussed the health of prehistoric man we were limited to the small amount of information to be obtained from fossilized bones. The Egyptians provide a much wider field for study in their consistent practice of mummification. The examination of mummies, by such authorities as Professor Elliot Smith, Sir Marc Armand Ruffer and Dr. F. Wood Jones, has produced knowledge of the greatest interest. Ruffer even evolved a technique, by means of which tissues dried three and four thousand years ago could be partially restored to the soft condition, and be examined under the microscope. In one case he demonstrated plainly the muscle fibres and cell nuclei in sand-dried pre-dynastic remains eight thousand years old.

The practice of mummification is of direct interest to our subject for it inevitably resulted in a detailed knowledge of the human body which other peoples could not possess. In fact, as Professor Elliot Smith points out, we know from the medical papyri "that the Egyptians had knowledge of certain parts of the body and their functions which for many centuries the Greeks lacked. Moreover, by familiarizing the embalmers with the properties of many resins, balsams and other . . . substances it gave them a knowledge of their antiseptic properties which afterwards led to their being included in the pharmacopœia."

Sir Armand Ruffer's *Studies in the Palæopathology of Egypt* brings out three facts of great interest. His microscopic examinations proved that, young as well as old, the Egyptians suffered as much as we do from hardening of the arteries, generally supposed to be a product of our busy, rushing modern life; the arterial lesions are identical with those found in twentieth-century patients. He can offer no reason for its prevalence three thousand and more years ago. Tobacco, alcohol, heavy meat diet, wear and tear—all the modern explanations—are examined and dismissed.

A second fact is the extraordinarily widespread evidence of the diseases which we group under the heading "arthritis." Spondylitis deformans (thickening and deformation of the spine, a condition already noted in prehistoric remains) was extremely common and often crippling. So also was arthritis deformans. Professor Elliot Smith declares that "arthritis is par excellence *the* bone disease of the ancient Egyptians and Nubian. . . . The pre-Dynastic Nubian scarcely ever grew to adult life without experiencing some of its effects." Sir Armand Ruffer found evidences of it in human remains in Upper and Lower Egypt from pre-dynastic times to the third century A.D., a period of at least eight thousand years during which arthritic disease was both chronic and common. There is even a case of it in a Miocene Period skeleton, going back some 900,000 years!

Why this painful and crippling disease should have spread so serious a blight on Egyptian health remains apparently a mystery. Climatic conditions, says Sir Armand Ruffer, can have no relation to it. Under-nutrition is also not an adequate reason, although there is evidence to show that during long periods great masses of the people were ill-fed and ill-housed. The condition of the fellahin to-day probably reflects something of that of their class in ancient times.

Modern medicine does not follow the older theories directly associating arthritic disease with damp and unhygienic conditions. Arthritis (joint inflammation) is regarded as due to infection, external or internal; osteo-arthritis, while not perfectly clear, is regarded as a degenerative change in joints subject to strain or injury and most common in those exposed to a rough life. May we, perhaps, find here a partial clue to the mystery, remembering that from the earliest to the latest times the glory of Egypt was its mighty monuments whose erection was the labour, mercilessly forced, of myriads of slaves of every generation? For instance, to haul an obelisk a short distance from its quarry five thousand men were employed under the lash of overseers. Diodorus states that 360,000 men were employed for twenty years in building a pyramid. Such brutal labours must have been conducive to every variety of strain and injury, particularly, under the stress of hauling, to the spine.

The third branch of Sir Armand Ruffer's studies which we are able to discuss here was an elaborate investigation of the condition of the teeth in Egyptian remains of all periods.

In modern times arthritic troubles are often associated with dental decay but, as Sudhoff puts it:

> Upon inspecting the many early Egyptian and Nubian crania we are astounded at the perfect preservation of the teeth, although the extensive abrasion of the masticatory surfaces is rather startling, suggesting simple, suitable fare, but mainly of vegetable character rich in cellulose and with a generous adulteration of sand particles.

This excessive wear resulted in exposing the pulp cavities of the teeth so that alveolar abscesses without dental caries are commonly found. Later, with softer and more luxurious feeding, dental decay appears. Tartar formation, caries and alveolar abscesses were found in some five hundred skeletons of aristocrats of the Third and Fourth Dynasties excavated at the Gizeh pyramids in proportions at least as common as those found in modern Europe. "And at every subsequent period of Egyptian history one finds the same thing—the wide prevalence of every form of dental disease among the wealthy of luxurious diet, and the relative immunity among the poorer people. . . . There is in no case the slightest suggestion that any operative and Thirteenth Dynasties though their subject matter is possibly many centuries older.

Egyptian magic is similar in principle and, to some extent in application, to that of the Assyrians which we have already discussed, and we shall therefore content ourselves with noting instances in which the papyri show advance towards scientific method. Since the older translations are unreliable we turn to the work of Mr. Warren Dawson and Professor J. H. Breasted, two modern Egyptologists, who have made some study of the texts. In the 875 recipes of the Ebers Papyrus there are only forty-seven diagnosed cases. Of these the most interesting are found in a section entitled "Directions for Illness of the Stomach," where symptoms, diagnosis and treatment are given for each of twenty cases. As Mr. Dawson justly observes in his *Magician and Leech*, "this collection of cases marks a great advance in real scientific observation and treatment." Each case begins "If you examine a man who suffers in the stomach" with a description of the symptoms, after which is the formula "You say concerning it: 'It is so and so'" (diagnosis). The treatment, with a prescription for drugs then follow. Unfortunately even this text is so corrupt (partly through being copied from older texts by scribes ignorant of their subject) that a direct translation which would be intelligible to a reader unacquainted with ancient Egyptian has been found impossible. The following rendering of one passage by M. Maspero gives a general idea of its nature:

If you have to deal with a patient (attacked) by an obstruction . . . if he feels heaviness after eating, if his stomach is full of wind, if his heart troubles him while walking as it does in the case of a patient suffering from anal fissure—examine him lying on his back, and if you find his stomach warm and some obstruction in the intestine say "something is wrong with the liver." Then give him the secret remedy of herbs which the doctor must mix himself.

Take the pulp of walnuts, and dates, mix, soak in water, make the patient drink it four mornings consecutively, to relieve and empty the stomach.

If after having done this you find the two hypochondria, that on the right warm, that on the left fresh (clear) say (about it): "The internal juices are fighting the evil which is destroying them!"

If on examining him a second time you find all the stomach clear, say "His liver is cured, it is cleansed, he has taken the remedy well."

The less scientific portions of the document where incantation and drug and treatment without diagnosis are mingled, include prescriptions for the bowels, intestinal worms, preven-

PLATE XI

TEMPLE OF ISIS AT PHILAE, A MEDICAL CENTRE

Besides the service of the gods many of the Egyptian temples were devoted to medical learning and the healing of the sick under the care of priest-physicians. As in the Asklepian temples of the Greeks, votive offerings and memorial tablets were deposited in the shrines. The photograph shows the temple of Isis at Philae before it was inundated.

Photo, Beato.

PLATE XI

PLATE XII

HYGIENE IN AN EGYPTIAN TOWN, 3,300 YEARS AGO

The town of Akhetaton, built by the heretic king Akhnaton of the 18th Dynasty (predecessor of the much-advertised Tutankhamen), was excavated by Professor T. E. Peet and Mr. C. L. Woolley. The private houses were well-ordered: in that of the nobleman Nekht were found (top) a bathroom, with sump and a drain, and (centre) a brazier stand, and a stand for water jars, for drinking and washing. The workmen's village, near the quarries, was crowded within a strong wall, each house containing four rooms—but no signs of hygienic convenience. Cleanliness was, apparently, the concern of noble, priest and official only.

By permission of the Egypt Exploration Society.

tion of vomiting, securing appetite and digestion, diseases of the eyes (a matter of even greater importance in Egypt than in Mesopotamia where eye troubles are common enough as we noted in page 17), lungs, liver, head and hair, mouth, teeth, tongue, throat and ear. Stiffness of the muscles and joints (obviously the rheumatoid complaints to whose widespread occurrence attention was drawn above) are dealt with in a long series of prescriptions.

The Egyptian pharmacopœia was an elaborate one and the art of pharmacy highly developed. Dr. Singer notes that "some thirty per cent of the crude vegetable drugs in the modern official pharmacopœia were known in antiquity." These include, of the hundreds of ingredients mentioned in the papyri, aloes, caraway, castor oil, coriander, dill, fennel, juniper, mint, myrrh and turpentine. One particularly interesting example is hartshorn, whose earliest use appears in Ebers where several prescriptions indicate powdered or burnt antlers or horns of stag, which as "spirits of hartshorn" (i.e. aqucous solution of ammonia) still appears in modern pharmacy. Hartshorn also appears in the Assyrian medical texts.

A section of the Ebers papyrus dealing with castor oil (which we have already seen in an Assyrian prescription, page 20) is of interest not merely as showing the use of a very familiar drug, but because, as Mr. Dawson points out, the passage which discusses it ranks as the earliest known fragment of a herbal. It shows considerable acquaintance with the virtues of the castor-oil plant (*Ricinus*). Mr. Dawson's rendering of this passage, which he describes as difficult and corrupt, is this:

> List of the virtues of *Ricinus ;* it was found in an ancient book concerning the things beneficial to mankind.
> If its rind be brayed in water and applied to a head that suffers, it will be cured immediately as if it had never been affected.
> If a few of its seeds be chewed with beer by a person who is constipated, it will expel the fæces from the body of that person.
> The hair of woman will be made to grow by means of its seed. Bray, mix and apply with grease. Let the woman anoint her head with it.
> Its oil is made from its seed. For anointing sores that emit a foul discharge. . . . Anoint very early in the morning in order to drive the (sores) away. A true remedy, proved millions of times.

Other prescriptions in the Ebers, Hearst and Berlin papyri employ it for purging, for head diseases and in fumigations and external applications.

D

One or two other examples which have been deciphered by Mr. Dawson from Ebers may be given. Intestinal troubles in addition to constipation were common. Here is an application for colic:

> Another for expelling illness from the side of the abdomen. *Efai* plant, 1; dates, 1; cook in fat. Bandage therewith.

A number of vermifuges appear, the rind of pomegranates pounded in water being frequently ordered, a use which survived for many centuries in East and West.

For the rheumatoid complaints referred to above the prescriptions bring out clearly the mixture of magic and reason, the rational element consisting of an ointment or emollient with an animal fat basis, and the magical of the addition of fats rare and difficult to obtain. The physician thereby added to the treatment that element of faith which has always been found effective. A characteristic remedy is this:

> Another for easing stiffness in any part of a man. Natron, 1; grease, the second day, 1; hippopotamus fat, 1; crocodile fat, 1; fat of *adu*-fish, 1; fat of silurus fish, 1; incense, 1; sweet frankincense, 1; honey, 1. Warm, bandage therewith.

If we are inclined to smile as members of a less credulous civilization at such foolish treatment let us consider the therapeutic use of the mouse. Among the many animal remedies found in the papyri we find the eating of a skinned mouse prescribed for an infantile complaint. Professor Elliot Smith speaks of the remains of mice which were discovered in the alimentary canal of child skeletons found in a pre-dynastic cemetery which dates back to about 4000 B.C. Evidently they were given in despair to children at the point of death. We smile; but the amusement changes to amazement when we learn that not only is there evidence for mouse medicine throughout classical and medieval times but that it has existed in the twentieth century. Mr. Dawson made personal acquaintance in 1925, and afterwards, of persons who, in their childhood, had swallowed skinned mice for the cure of whooping cough and other child ailments.

On the whole, however, Egyptian medicine is worthy of more respect than such items suggest, especially in respect to methods of treatment and application of remedies. The directions given in the papyri prescriptions as to the administration of the drugs are entirely modern in character. The quantities are minutely specified in the prescriptions, the patient is instructed how often to take the medicine, whether at night or morning, before or after food and for how many days (not more than four in acute cases, when the treatment had to be changed).

Medicine is administered in milk, water, honey, wine or beer. There is an impressively modern array of treatments and remedies in Ebers and other papyri, including bandages, poultices, plasters, pills, pastilles, suppositories, enemata, gargles, inhalations, fumigations, snuffs, salves, ointments and emollients of many kinds.

The Edwin Smith papyrus which has only recently been studied and translated by Professor J. H. Breasted, although it was discovered at the same time as the Ebers papyrus, is of greater interest than all the other papyri. Its chief authority considers it "the torso of a great lost medical book on surgery and external medicine." Its contents are mainly surgical, consisting of forty-seven cases which begin with the top of the head and proceed systematically downward breaking off suddenly in the forty-eighth case dealing with the spine. The cases are arranged in a standard order thus:

Title : " Instructions concerning a wound in the ear.

Examination : If thou examinest a man having a wound in his ear cutting through its flesh, the injury being in the lower part of his ear, and confined to the flesh, thou shouldest draw it together for him with stitching behind the hollow of his ear.

Diagnosis : Thou shouldest say concerning him: a sufferer having a wound in his ear.

Verdict, one of three: (1) " It is an ailment I will treat "; or (2) " It is an ailment I will contend with "; or (3) " An ailment I will not treat."

More scientific in his outlook than the all-powerful magician, the physician-surgeon, saw clearly the limits of his powers; as Dr. Marett puts it, his is a department in which the peculiar effects of the faith cure are never likely to be prominent at any stage of human progress. In the first case he is confident of the outcome, in the second he recognizes serious trouble and in the third he abandons hope. Only thirteen of the forty-seven cases described receive the last verdict.

The medical aspects of this papyrus are few, but Professor Breasted's elucidations of them may be summarized. Wounds and bruises are healed by the application of fresh meat (*cf.* the modern housewife's beefsteak for a black eye) followed after the first day by honey ointment and an astringent herb. Surely a sound enough treatment—and it is three thousand five hundred years old in this text.

The physician's attitude was largely one of co-operation with nature. Repeatedly the writer of this text, the ancient authority, directs the practitioner to do nothing but put the patient on normal diet and await results. The words of this instruction are curious. The expression is, "put the patient on his fingers" and even the Egyptian copyist of the seventeenth century B.C. found this expression strange, so he adds the comment: "it means—to put him on his accustomed food without giving him medical treatment." The idiom is probably connected with the notion of eating with the fingers.

The other two papyri to which reference has been made, the Hearst and the Berlin, have little further material of interest to our study, being similar in character to the Ebers papyrus. The Hearst papyrus came from a ruined house in a small provincial town and Dr. Offord considers that it "was probably an inexpensive copy of the then common medical treatise possessed by a country doctor for his daily use."

If we could end on the note struck by the Edwin Smith papyrus and infer a gradual progress in medical science, or even a maintenance of the standard reached, Egyptian medicine would stand as high or even higher in our estimation as it did in that of the ancient world. Unhappily we cannot. In the New Kingdom and the Empire, the days of the Thothmes and Amenhoteps (including the short reign of the insignificant Tutankhamen) of the Eighteenth Dynasty, and the two Rameses of the Nineteenth, magic and incantation re-appear. As Professor T. E. Peet remarks: "On medicine as on religion magic laid its devastating touch. Medical science was already old in the Middle Kingdom and yet it made no advance from that time onward. Magic had stopped its growth." We have seen above that all the indications are that the best and most scientific portions of the medical papyri now in existence are copied from much more ancient texts.

If magic stopped the growth of medicine religion may claim to have given medicine better service. The priest-physicians not only kept alight and handed on from century to century the lamp of medical learning but devoted their temples to the service of the sick as well as of the gods to whom they were dedicated [Plate 11]. Here we may possibly see partial anticipations

of those temples of healing which under the Greeks nearly
became effective hospitals. Dr. Jayne, in his *Healing Gods of
Ancient Civilizations*, says:

> There were many healing temples in the Valley, but eventually
> all the great medical centres were located at the chief capitals
> along the Nile, and large numbers of people travelling . . . and
> making annual pilgrimages, sought the curative influences of their
> favourite deities. . . . These healing shrines were depositories
> of medical lore. . . . On the walls of the sanctuaries were
> inscriptions and votive tablets in commemoration of miraculous
> cures and round about, in the precincts, steles and statues erected
> by former patients in grateful recognition of cures effected by the
> divinity. Here priests and lay brethren who were to practise heal-
> ing pursued their studies and took their oath.

Finally we must give some consideration to the hygiene
practised in Egypt which in the eyes of the classical world, if
Herodotus reports accurately, ranked even higher than their
therapeutics. One suspects that, excellent as it probably was,
Egyptian hygiene concerned itself principally with king, priest
and noble. In the great township of Akhetaton at El Amarna,
built by the heretic king Akhnaton about 1370 B.C., remains of
bathrooms and drainage systems are found in the fine houses
of vizier, noble and priest, but none in the close-packed dwell-
ings of the workmen at the quarries [Plate 12]. Similarly in the
earlier Middle Kingdom (Twelfth Dynasty) town of Illahun,
the lay-out of the mansions is spacious but the workmen's
houses are crowded behind a thick wall.

Certainly hygiene reached a high stage of development which
could not have been without some influence on the life of the
people. Divine ordinations regulated public and individual
cleanliness in dwelling and person. Many temple inscriptions
promised health and long life to the clean and temperate. The
priests set the standard, with their baths every six hours, their
body shaving at three-day intervals and their spotless white
clothing. On the public side they provided a ritual form of
meat inspection before and after slaughter which, while intended
to preserve the purity of the sacrifice, assisted public health,
since rejected meat would not be eaten. There was some
recognition of the value of prevention of disease for, deriving
most disease from dietary error, they observed a form of
prophylaxis, at least in Herodotus' time, in the custom of
administering emetics and enemata for three consecutive days
each month.

in the Ægean completed in Crete the destruction begun by earlier earthquake calamities, when Troy fell and Egypt under the Twentieth Dynasty was definitely on the down grade.

If it were possible to interpret the Minoan texts we should doubtless find matter of medical interest which would throw light on later Greek developments. Although we have plenty of evidence of Minoan intercourse with Egypt (practically the whole system of Minoan dating depends on Egyptian contacts) there is none of culture debts to Egypt; rather does it appear that Egypt borrowed from Crete. What, therefore, of culture the Greeks derived from Crete, either directly, or indirectly through Mycenæ, would have little tinge of Egypt.

Until the Cretan alphabet gives up its key we must be content with material evidence, mainly hygienic, of interest to our inquiry. In the Early Period we find nothing, but in the Middle Minoan Period whence dates the first great palace of Knossos we find an advanced architecture coupled with the initiation of a drainage system excelling any practised in the ancient world, except by the Romans. In the Late Period (from 1600—1200 B.C.) the great temple-palace of Knossos displays its final wonders. Its labyrinthine structure, its great pillared halls, its stairways, its sanitary contrivances, give an astonishing picture of the wealth, power and scientific progress of this early island state which ruled the whole Ægean area, including its coast lands.

The excavations of Sir Arthur Evans at Knossos, described in his great work *The Palace of Minos*, have brought to light several interesting examples of Minoan sanitation of which the following may be quoted.

The palace of the first Middle Period (M.M. I) was supplied with water by means of pipes which were, it is said, better adapted for preventing the accumulation of sediment than the water pipes of modern cities [Plate 14].

Of the second Period (M.M. II) Sir Arthur Evans says:

> It is not too much to say that comfort and luxury were studied with a greater completeness than ever before in the history of the world. Thus the palace had a system of sanitation superior to that of any other ancient civilisation; superior indeed to that of any medieval city.

In his 1929-30 excavations Sir Arthur discovered a series of immense stone-lined pits (*koloura*) which had been constructed in the M.M. II Period (over ruins of houses of the previous Period) for the sole purpose of disposing of the city's rubbish [Plate 13].

PLATE XIII
City Sanitation in Minoan Crete, c. 1900 b.c.

In the wonderful city of Knossos, with its great Palace of Minos, excavated and restored by Sir Arthur Evans, circular walled pits of large size, called *kouloura*, were constructed for the sanitary disposal of rubbish from the Palace area. Earth was apparently used in layers to prevent effluvia, and a certain amount of surface water was drained into them. These most effective public rubbish dumps, arranged in line, were built in the M.M. II Period (1900-1750 b.c.) on the ruins of houses of the previous Period.

Courtesy of Sir Arthur Evans.

PLATE XIII

PLATE XIV

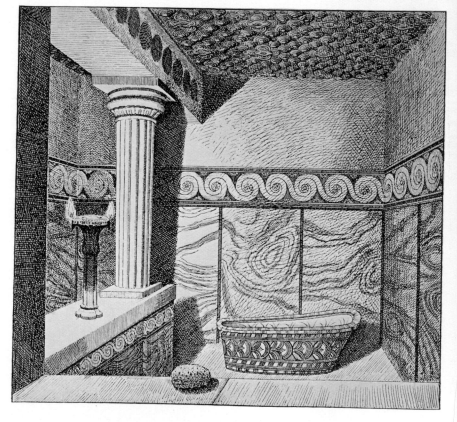

PLATE XIV

Personal Hygiene in the Minoan Palace of Knossos

In the Queen's apartment an ornate bathroom has recently been found and restored by Sir Arthur Evans; it dated from the Late Minoan II period (c. 1400 B.C.). Its painted terra-cotta hip bath was filled and emptied by hand. An earlier type of bath (of M.M. III period) is shown above. A remarkable water main, even earlier (M.M. I, about 2160 B.C.), was made of terra-cotta. As seen, it had collars and top ridges, and each section was of tapering form that "gave a shooting motion to the water and prevented sediment." "These pipes," says Sir Arthur Evans, "show an advance on nearly all modern systems of earthenware pipes" with parallel sections. As related in page 225 efficient earthenware pipes were only re-invented in England in the late nineteenth century—4,000 years later.

From Evans, "The Palace of Minos", Macmillan & Co., Ltd.

PLATE XIV

PERSONAL HYGIENE IN THE MINOAN PALACE OF KNOSSOS

In the Queen's apartment an ornate bathroom has recently been found and restored by Sir Arthur Evans; it dated from the Late Minoan II period (c. 1400 B.C.). Its painted terra-cotta hip bath was filled and emptied by hand. An earlier type of bath (of M.M. III period) is shown above. A remarkable water main, even earlier (M.M. I, about 2160 B.C.), was made of terra-cotta. As seen, it had collars and top ridges, and each section was of tapering form that "gave a shooting motion to the water and prevented sediment." "These pipes," says Sir Arthur Evans, "show an advance on nearly all modern systems of earthenware pipes" with parallel sections. As related in page 223 efficient earthenware pipes were only re-invented in England in the late nineteenth century—4,000 years later.

From Evans, "The Palace of Minos," Macmillan & Co., Ltd.

Throughout the Middle and Late Periods all the bigger houses of Minoan Crete, whether at Knossos or the other settlements on the island, were fitted with bathrooms with clay pottery hip baths of curiously modern shape. Indications have even been found of a hot water supply. In one large house, probably belonging to a court official, near the palace a lustral (ritual) area of the last Middle Period (M.M. III) was in the next (L.M. I) filled in—

> and its conversion into what looks like that of an ordinary bathroom resembling that of the Domestic Quarter, is a significant circumstance. It looks as if the ordinary conveniences of domestic life were beginning to outweigh religious ceremonial.—(*Evans.*)

The queen's bathroom in the L.M. II palace, as restored by Sir Arthur Evans, is a marvel of spaciousness which would do credit to any modern mansion [Plate 14].

Cretan sanitation of the last two periods (L.M. II-III) may be regarded as a model. We have a measure of the Minoan achievement when we consider that the rest of Europe during this time (1450–1200 B.C.) was still inhabited by nomadic and migrating barbarian peoples of the Bronze Age, and that even in Egypt iron, the principal material element in all our modern civilization (for we are now in the Iron Age), did not come into use until the end of this period. Sanitation is one of the last teachings to reach even civilized peoples but the Minoans possessed it over three thousand years ago.

On the river side of the great palace was a sewage system designed both as a means of disposing of surface water and, by connecting the rain conduits with the water closets, etc., as a method of obtaining water-borne sewage. Large cut stone shafts, cement lined, descended vertically from the upper stories of the "domestic quarter" and opened into large stone conduits which brought the rain water to the drains, ventilated the sewers and gave access for cleansing. Their very water closets resembled the modern wash-out type, i.e. they always had water in the pan. Apparently they were provided with wooden seats.

The excellence of their sanitation makes keener the regret that the long failure to solve the difficult puzzle of their script renders impossible any investigation of their medical knowledge. At any rate it is fairly clear that here was the main source of the hygienic ideas of the Greeks.

We learn nothing fresh of importance from the Mycenæan remains of the mainland so that jumping a period of nearly six hundred years we turn to the Greeks of the seventh–sixth century B.C.

Our main underlying purpose here is to bring out the fact that we are now dealing with people—thinkers, scientists, practitioners—whom we may meet on our own ground, whose ideas and observations need no translation for our easy comprehension. We do not see those ideas mistily as though a veil as we do the definitely strange and foreign thought of Babylonian and Egyptian.

In Greek thought everything is clear cut, its outlines hard and sharp with no mystification of idea-arresting magic, no prohibition of priest-ridden religion. There is, in their religion, no dominance of a priestly hierarchy. Science is saved from dogmatism. In the earlier peoples it is a matter for surprise that with all their handicaps they achieved so much so many thousands of years ago. But with the Greeks it seems natural and obvious that we should find them taking all knowledge for their province and pursuing it by means so scientific in essence that in respect of many principles and bases all the culture and enquiry of the succeeding ages has found no need or room for improvement. With sure and serene wisdom untrammelled by the heavy cloak of magical theory, tradition, or tabu, they practised a system of medicine so soundly based that modern medicine owes it a debt whose value can hardly be exaggerated. In fact we appear to emerge, with the abruptness of a train coming out of a tunnel, from the noisome darkness of superstition into the healthy sunshine of science. Though the simile is not inapposite it presents, however, but a part of the picture, though the greater part, as will appear later.

In this present century we have heard much of protest against the dead hand of the classics. In other times formalism which sought to keep inviolate and sacrosanct the *ipsissima verba* of the Hippocratic and Galenic texts, imperfectly comprehended, inspired revolt against the written word written so long before. Nevertheless critical and unbiased examination of what remains of the original texts leaves the unescapeable conclusion that all, rebels, pioneers and pupils alike, are inheritors of the Greeks. A leading medical historian has accurately summarized the position:

> Without Herophilus we should have had no Harvey and the rise of physiology might have been delayed for centuries; had Galen's works not survived, Vesalius would never have reconstructed Anatomy, and Surgery too might have stayed behind with

her laggard sister, Medicine; the Hippocratic collection was the
necessary and acknowledged basis for the work of the greatest of
modern clinical observers, Thomas Sydenham, and the teaching
of Hippocrates and of his school is the substantial basis of instruction in the wards of a modern hospital.—(*Charles Singer*, " The
Legacy of Greece.")

Let it here be observed, as may be necessary, that while the
case is in no way overstated it is based solely (and legitimately)
on the products of the best Greek minds. The group of peoples
known generically as the Greeks was in reality a complex mixing
of races varying widely in origin, culture and mental attributes.
So lacking in homogeneity was the mixture that in fact it never
did blend properly, and the outstanding fact in Greek history
is the perpetual jealous quarrelling of city with city and state
with state, that in a very few centuries brought the whole polity
to ruin and to Macedonian and Roman subjection. The Greek
civilization was one of quick and brilliant achievement but, with
all its lasting glory, unstable as a national entity and full of
flaws.

So we find naturally enough that the Oriental heritage, both
from Mesopotamian and Egyptian sources as well as the farther
East, of magic and non-rational medicine was not lost and that
these elements appear in some of the Greek writings, particularly those of later date. We need give them no consideration
for they have no relation to the purely scientific literature with
its observation and classifications of disease, its sound generaliza-
tions and its reasoned treatments. We shall, however, have to
consider the pseudo-miraculous "incubation" cures of the
Asklepian temples.

Who, then, were these remarkable peoples? Minoans,
Mycenæans, Achæans—these were perhaps the principal races
of origin. Later we find Æolian, Ionian, Dorian and Attic
peoples with many sub-races and tribes. Fortunately we are
not concerned to give a precise answer to a question which
has long engaged the attention of scholars and still continues to
do so.

Of the races mentioned the Ionians and Dorians are the only
peoples who figure prominently in the medical picture. Between
them they are to be credited with the greater part of the best
works of the early Greek intellect, and men of their race are
mainly responsible for the Greek medical system. Cos and
Cnidus, the centres of early medical teaching, were Dorian
colonies which included large numbers of Ionians among

their inhabitants. The Hippocratic books are written throughout in the Ionian literary dialect.

In these early, pre-Hippocratic days, a few philosophers and physicians stand out and in them we see the beginnings of the growth that led to the supremacy of the fifth century. For though we have, as has been said, the sensation of a sudden emergence from the twilight of magic-soiled medicine to the daylight of science, nothing in evolution, whether of peoples or plants is really sudden. The speculating, varied Greek mind compounded of heterogeneous racial origins and influences exhibited a breadth of outlook that inspired a dispassionate, detached appreciation of native and foreign ideas and customs. Culture attained its highest early development in the great commercial centres that arose in Ionia, then the connecting link with Egypt and the East, and many foreign elements are found in the free-thinking Ionian natural philosophy. So the Greek inquirer, while maintaining his critical attitude, secured the best of Egyptian and Assyro-Babylonian medical ideas, methods and drugs.

In the seventh century B.C., as we have seen in earlier pages, Ashurbanipal of Assyria was collecting in his great library at Nineveh all the medical lore of his kingdom. Towards the end of the same century we may see the dawn of genuine medical science. It probably began at Cnidus in Asia Minor, where, in the earliest Greek medical school, the facts of disease—not magical notions or arbitrary, empirical ideas, but properly observed facts—were collected, classified and recorded in "sentences" or aphorisms now lost. The teachers of this school are said, by the critics of the great rival school at Cos, to have treated symptom rather than patient and to have been faulty in prognosis: nevertheless although their writings are lost some of their doctrines are to be found in the Hippocratic books, a number of which show their influence. According to Hippocrates they invented the names pleurisy (*pleuritis*) pneumonia (*peripneumonia*) and *phrenitis*.

The teachers of Cos, a school of somewhat later foundation, were distinguished by emphasis on prognosis, the careful investigation of the condition of the patient rather than the symptoms of his disease and a reliance on the healing powers of nature in preference to vigorous treatment. Between them these two great schools, inheriting and developing the principles of Ionian philosophy, share the greater part of the credit for the splendour of Greek medical achievement.

Under the conditions of the time and in the absence of any bulk of detailed knowledge the Cnidian method of detailed classification of disease by symptoms was bound to be unsuccessful, though in principle scientific, for they carried differentiation to extremes and failed in practical treatment. They had no sympathy with the general pathology of Hippocrates which his scientific genius, working with the admittedly limited knowledge of the age, elevated to an amazingly successful medical system. As Mr. W. H. S. Jones says, in the Loeb edition of the Hippocratic works, "Hippocrates did the wrong thing well: the Cnidians did the right thing badly. . . . . A dislike of theory, a careful cataloguing of symptoms . . . are characteristics that appear in several of the works in the Corpus generally considered Cnidian." He considers that Cnidian doctrine influenced medicine generally. Hippocrates himself came from a family of physicians in the island of Cos and the main principles and tendencies of Coan teaching in the fifth and fourth centuries B.C. are represented in the great Hippocratic Collection.

Before we consider the monumental work of Hippocrates and his school we must note a few of the more important ideas and principles worked out by other and earlier philosophers. Among the Ionian school of nature philosophers in the sixth century B.C. Anaximenes of Miletus and Heraclitus of Ephesus (who was perhaps a physician) propounded the doctrines of air as the primary principle with "pneuma" as the breath of life and heat and moisture with their opposites as fundamental qualities of the body. These doctrines were further developed in the South Italian (Sicilian) school. The strongest personality in the famous medical school of Croton, founded by Pythagoras of Samos in the late sixth century, was Empedocles of Agrigentum made known to every schoolboy of the last generation at least by Matthew Arnold's poem. Physician and physiologist, poet and traveller, his influence was wide, and his teaching of the four elements (earth, air, fire and water) and the four qualities (heat, cold, moisture and dryness) finally produced that sterile doctrine of the "humours" of the body, which, as we shall see in the medieval section of this work, dominated medicine until, after the Renaissance, Greek science came into the light again.

Empedocles, however, cannot be held responsible for medieval futilities. With his contemporary, Alcmæon of Croton, he developed the important principle that health depends upon harmony of the elements within the body and disease upon their discord. He also taught that "the blood is the life" and the seat of "innate heat" which he seems to have identified with the soul. The heart he regarded as the centre of the body system and the chief organ of the "pneuma" of Anaximenes. Pneuma and air pervade the universe and the pneumatic school of physiology, which became of importance later, is due to the philosophical speculations of Empedocles.

More obviously striking perhaps were his hygienic achievements. He seems to have realized that swamp and marsh produce disease for he earned great fame by checking a plague of malaria which devastated the Sicilian town of Selinos about 480 B.C. by the expedient of joining together the two streams of the district and so (apparently) draining the marshes. Whatever he did, the pestilence was stayed, and the grateful people struck a number of beautiful coins to commemorate the city's deliverance [see Plate 15]; twelve examples of the coins are now in the British Museum.

Another outstanding personality of the pre-Hippocratic period is that of Democedes, the first physician of whom we have a trustworthy history. He was born about 520 B.C., and according to Herodotus was an extremely successful public medical officer. His career shows that there was a public medical service well organized and regarded as being of high importance in the second half of the sixth century, at least two generations before Hippocrates. In his second year as state physician of Ægina Democedes received a salary of one talent, almost equal to £500 in our money. He then spent a year at Athens at an increased fee, and in the fourth year Polycrates, tyrant of Samos, secured his services at double the rate paid by Ægina. Public inscriptions tell us of equal honours paid to other physicians. These state physicians were clearly distinguished men whose services were much esteemed and keenly sought for. They were entirely secular and independent of the Asklepieion temples. References to their election by popular assembly occur in Plato's *Dialogues*. They may be seen at work in fifth century vase paintings [Plate 20].

The form of public medical treatment which engages the attention of most popular writers on medicine in ancient Greece, and to which, perhaps, undue prominence has been given in the past, is that of the priestly, semi-religious rites of the temple of Asklepios, the Roman Æsculapius. Certainly the material remains bulk largely. Over three hundred temples to Asklepios are known to have been built. The finest ruins are those of the temple at Epidaurus [Plate 15] which was perhaps the greatest centre of the cult. The festivals there were so popular that the buildings included a theatre—one of the most beautiful Greek structures that remain—which would hold twenty thousand spectators, and a stadium seating twelve thousand. Dr. Caton in his restoration of the ruins of the Asklepieion, shows in addition among the many buildings a central shrine of Asklepios, another to his daughter Hygeia, a great abaton (the sleeping place for the sick), baths, hostels and a probable library site.

Obviously a highly successful and wealthy centre. Excavations at Cos have shown that the Asklepieion there was almost equally successful. The treatment supplied must therefore have been one of direct appeal to the masses of the people and since it was, in a large degree, faith-healing we can understand its success.

Other centres of which Greek ruins persist are to be seen at Athens, Pergamos and even as far afield as Butrino in Albania. As we have seen similar temples devoted to the gods of healing and the service of the sick existed in Egypt and, judging by votive offerings and other records, a system of treatment not greatly dissimilar was in vogue.

These temples probably date from the eighth or early seventh centuries B.C. Their patron, the divine Asklepios, whose serpent still remains the emblem of healing [Plate 18], was a chief of Thessaly who fought in the Trojan Wars. His two sons are described by Homer as skilled physicians. By 770 B.C. a Greek poet, Arctinus, invests him with supernatural attributes and soon after the temple worship began. In them developed a semi-miraculous system of treatment known as "incubation".

The "incubation" sleep, in which the god gave the sleeping patient instructions for his cure, or performed the cure itself, was the main part of the ritual of treatment. After performing certain sacrifices and ritual washings the patient lay down at night in the abaton, an airy sleeping chamber open on the south side, an arrangement that probably did much to bring credit to the god by assisting recovery [Plate 16]. The priest recited prayers begging for divine help for the sick. According to the inscriptions the god frequently appeared in the dreams of the patient, or in person, diagnosed his ailment and spoke of its treatment. Probably the priest himself in the dim light acted the part of the god and it seems likely that the patient was also drugged or narcotized. The treatment is described in the *Plutus* of Aristophanes, and despite the poet's satire it is a clear account of the ritual employed. Perhaps the modern study of dreams may be regarded as in some small part a reversion to Asklepian methods. Of the nature of the cases treated and the cures achieved some of the votive tablets from Epidaurus give a reasonably fair idea. We quote a few.

A man who had only one eye is visited by the god in the abaton. The god applies an ointment to the empty orbit. On awakening the man finds he has two sound eyes.—(*Caton.*)

Heraicus of Mytilene is bald and entreats the god to make his hair grow. An ointment is applied by Asklepios, and the next morning he has a thick crop of hair.

These are certainly cases of miracle-mongering, and we need expend no space in their discussion. Another type of case is susceptible of the explanation already suggested that the priest masqueraded as the god since he obviously performed the operation described:

A man had an abdominal abscess. He saw a vision and thought that the god ordered the slaves that accompanied him to lift him up and hold him, so that his abdomen could be cut open. The man tried to get away, but his slaves caught him and bound him. So Asklepios cut him open, rid him of the abscess, and then stitched him up again, releasing him from his bonds. Straightway he departed cured, and the floor of the abaton was covered with blood.— (*Hamilton.*)

In another case dropsy is treated in the truly heroic manner. Asklepios (according to the patient's dream as described in the inscription) cuts off the patient's head, holds him upside down to let the fluid run out and then replaces the head! A simpler case of faith-healing is probably revealed in the following invocation:

Oh, blessed Asklepios, God of Healing, it is thanks to thy skill that Diophantes hopes to be relieved from his incurable and horrible gout, no longer to move like a crab, no longer to walk upon thorns, but to have sound feet as thou hast decreed.

In later times, as Dr. Caton points out, superstition and semi-fraud gave way to a larger extent to genuine healing. The earlier priests prescribed "many things that were prudent and judicious; plain and simple diet, hot and cold baths, poulticing for certain chest ailments and a variety of medicaments."

In the Asklepieion some have seen a prototype of the modern hospital, since patients were received for periods of different length, and attention was paid to diet, exercise, massage and bathing. It is a point worthy of remark that these temples flourished in places that were natural health resorts, some with mineral or hot springs as well. Moreover secular Asklepiads

PLATE XV

When Empedocles Stayed the Malaria Plague

These coins of Selinos, Sicily, are believed to have been struck about 480 B.C., to commemorate the deliverance of the city from a malaria plague by the action of Empedocles (*see* page 46). Both coins show sacrifice being offered to Asklepios and a leaf of the wild celery, after which the town was named.

On the obverse of one coin Apollo is seen in his chariot shooting the health-giving arrows—the sun's rays—and on the other Heracles subduing the Cretan Bull.

British Museum.

Reconstruction of the Asklepian Temple Buildings at Epidaurus

This reconstruction, based on the excavations of the Greek Archæological Society of the extensive ruins at Epidaurus, shows, on the left, the Tholos or rotunda: in the centre, the Abaton where the patients slept: and on the right, the temple of the god. There were also many other buildings in this very successful centre of healing and miracle. The ruins of the great Theatre are among the most beautiful that exist in Greece.

From " Monuments Antiques".

PLATE XV

PLATE XVI

PLATE XVI
WHERE THE ASKLEPIAN CURES WERE WROUGHT

In this reconstruction drawing, after Dr. Caton, the interior of the Abaton, or open-fronted portico, is seen. Here the patients slept, and during their sleep the god visited them in their dreams and indicated or completed the cure desired. One patient stands before an altar making his offering to the priests, while the sacred serpent licks his wound.

After Caton " Temples and Ritual of Asklepios at Epidaurus."

were apparently attached who were free from the temple super-
stitions and its theurgic rites. Hippocrates himself was an
Asklepiad of Cos. But while the temples may be supposed to
have provided rich clinical material for study—and indeed Pliny
and Strabo both declare that Hippocrates was indebted to the
temple tablets describing disease—there seems no doubt that the
Asklepiads were not priests, but probably a guild, and that Greek
medicine owes little if anything to the temples.

Dr. Withington is of opinion that if the inscriptions at Cos
resembled those found at Epidaurus, they can only have warned
Hippocrates what a clinical history should not be.

Greek medicine in fact like other Greek activities was so little
hampered by bonds of any kind that its forms of practice were
manifold. In addition to the priests of the Asklepian temples
and the state physicians we have, before Hippocrates, several
other classes of healers including the philosophers, gymnastic
trainers (who were consulted in diet questions, injuries, exercises
and massage), various forms of empirics and quacks, medicinal
root collectors, pharmacopolists or druggists (of somewhat
sinister significance since the word *pharmakon*, a medicine or
remedy, originally meant a poison), and even "wise women"
and midwives of none too savoury a reputation.

By the middle of the fifth century genuine Greek medicine
and the limited knowledge and experience it had laboriously
acquired was in danger of being lost in a quagmire of sophistry
and speculative philosophy, with its unverified postulates and
charlatanry, such as actually overwhelmed it in the Dark Ages.
Then with the appearance of the mysterious, towering figure
of the great Father of Medicine and his followers and pupils
"the Art" becomes a free and unfettered profession and Hellenic
medicine attains a high measure of rational science and an even
greater moral dignity.

Of Greek hygiene in the Golden Age and later little more than
generalities can be given. Archæology has given most of her
attention to the temples, and no one has done for the domestic
architecture of the Greeks what Sir Arthur Evans has done for
that of the Cretans. Wiegand has examined the ruins of the small
towns of Priene and Miletus in Asia Minor but they are mainly
of the later, Hellenistic, period. At Priene water-closets of modern
type were discovered. The following information is mainly from
literary sources. Each house of more than moderate means had
a room set aside for bathing, which was placed outside and near
the terrace. Large houses had great stone basins. After exercise

E

or fatigue of any kind the Greek took a bath, generally hot; cold baths were considered tonic.

Aristophanes characterizes a person unable to get a bath as "poor and dirty." He must have been for there were public baths (two oboles entrance fee) as well as private, and Herodotus speaks of hot-air baths. Bathing is a frequent subject of the vase paintings, including public baths for women, as may be seen on vases in the British Museum and the Louvre. Baths were attached to all the great gymnasia.

Lucien says that the house directed towards the East was considered the best. The windows were to be open to all points of the horizon to ensure that the house was bright, bathed in the rays of the sun and also well-aired and ventilated thereby.

Matters of public hygiene were the concern of city officers. Town planning, street arrangement, water supply and sewage disposal were all considered and regulated, particularly under Pericles and other Tyrants in the fifth century. Plato in his *Laws* discusses the necessity for the canalization of soiled water and the free supply of good water. The drains and sewers of Athens are said to have been well constructed. The great sewer ended in a tank, from which brick conduits distributed the contents over open ground well outside the city.

CHAPTER V

GREECE: THE FATHER OF ALL MEDICINE

Vita brevis, ars longa est. ' Life is short, the Art long,' opportunity fleeting, experience treacherous/or, deceptive/judgement
difficult. The physician must be ready, not only to do his
duty himself, but also to secure the co-operation of the patient,
of the attendants and of the externals.

THIS, PERHAPS the most famous of all the "Aphorisms" of
the Hippocratic Collection, together with the great Hippocratic
Oath itself, exposes a creed that raises professional medical
ethic and professional medical method to the highest pinnacle
of aspiration, the symbol of the highest ideal and the embodi-
ment of a new era of immortal power in the quest for health.

Hippocrates was born in the island of Cos about 400 B.C.,
the son of an Asklepiad, and a pupil, and later a teacher, in the
medical school of Cos. Beyond the facts that he travelled
widely, possibly lived a while in Athens, and died at Larisa at
the great age of—according to different traditions—from eighty-
five to one hundred and nine years we know nothing in detail
of his actual life. His fame is almost beyond recounting. Even
in his lifetime he was known as "the Great" and Plato placed
him in equality with two of the master artists of all time—
Polycletus and Pheidias. His shadowy figure is behind all
Greek medical writing and the best practice till barbarian
darkness descends [Plate 19].

His period, it is perhaps worth recalling obvious though it
be, is that of the high tide, the full flower of Hellenic life. The
glorious fifth century saw the incomparable achievements of
Pericles and Socrates, Plato, Thucydides, Sophocles, Euripides,
Aristophanes, Pheidias, Polycletus and Praxiteles and many
another of the great ones, the mere mention of whose names is
almost an inclusive catalogue of human intellectual capacity.

When we speak of Hippocrates and his school it is difficult
to avoid the appearance of easy and fulsome laudation. Let us
first notice the conditions and limitations of contemporary

medicine. The Greek knew nothing of bacteria and infection (although the Hippocratic work *Epidemics* acknowledges that consumption is contagious while stating that fevers are not), his *apparatus medicus* was primitive by modern standards, and his actual store of medical knowledge was necessarily small, for but little time had been available for the accumulation of pathological facts. He knew something of disease and the course it ran, and even of its cure. Many parts of the Hippocratic books are open to criticism or even condemnation by our standards. There is also a mixture of medicine and sophistic philosophy in them which represents one of the main obstacles to steady scientific advance at that time.

Superstition and divine notions of disease had been relegated to quacks and the temples. Then came philosophy with its perpetual search for uniformity in the chaos of unordered natural phenomena and endeavoured to include medicine within the scope of its soaring guesswork. Philosophy is even now but rarely in touch with the dull, plodding, fact-by-fact registration of science. Then it never was. The Greek word hypothesis (*upothesis*) was not that used by the modern man of science who, having accumulated and ordered his facts, frames a hypothesis to account for them. Plato and the Sophists started with a hypothesis on which their scheme of ideas was erected, just as the beautifully ordered propositions of Euclid depend upon certain unverifiable axioms or postulates. The Greek *upothesis* is, therefore, best translated as 'postulate.' Such *a priori* assumptions are useless in science and dangerously useless in medicine. Celsus, the Roman medical writer, ascribes to Hippocrates the credit for the separation of medicine from philosophy, and the six or seven books of the Hippocratic Canon are as free from the sophistry of the philosophers as they are from the dogmas of religion which sterilized all earlier tendencies to scientific progress.

It is not necessary to dilate further upon the failings of Greek medicine. As in our own time, so throughout the fifth century and later periods, quackery and charlatanry, magic and sophistry, flourished alongside science. There was no state control and any person could set up as a healer without qualification. There remain the incontrovertible facts that for over two thousand four hundred years Hippocrates has been acknowledged as the Father of Medicine, and that the Hippocratic ethic established the highest set of ideals, still acclaimed by the profession the world round.

The ethical keynote is struck by the great Oath of Service laid upon the neophyte which, in the twentieth century, still shines as a beacon light and is still incorporated in the teachings of not a few European medical schools. It has so often been quoted that to the student of medical history it is a glorious commonplace, but it cannot be omitted here. The translation that follows is taken from Mr. W. H. S. Jones' edition of *Hippocrates:*

> I swear by Apollo Physician, by Asclepius, by Health, by Panacea, and by all the gods and goddesses, making them my witnesses, that I will carry out, according to my ability and judgement this oath and this indenture.
>
> To hold my teacher in this art equal to my own parents; to make him partner in my livelihood; when he is in need of money to share mine with him; to consider his family as my own brothers and to teach them this art, if they want to learn it, without fee or indenture; to impart precept, oral instruction, and all other instruction to my own sons, the sons of my teacher, and to indentured pupils, but to nobody else.
>
> I will use treatment to help the sick according to my ability and judgement, but never with a view to injury and wrong-doing.
>
> Neither will I administer a poison to anybody when asked to do so, nor will I suggest such a course. Similarly I will not give a woman a pessary to cause abortion. But I will keep pure and holy both my life and my art.
>
> I will not use the knife, not even, verily, on sufferers from stone, but I will give place to such as are craftsmen therein.
>
> Into whatsoever houses I enter I will enter to help the sick and I will abstain from all intentional wrong-doing and harm, especially from abusing the bodies of man or woman, bond or free.
>
> And whatsoever I shall see or hear in the course of my profession, as well as outside my profession in my intercourse with men, if it be what should not be published abroad I will never divulge, holding such things to be holy secrets.
>
> Now if I carry out this oath and break it not, may I gain for ever reputation among all men for my life and for my art; but if I transgress it and forswear myself, may the opposite befall me.

The origin and particular application of these noble rules are matters for the controversy of scholars. We need only note that they are genuinely Hippocratic. The phrase "I will keep holy both my life and my art" is of special interest. Throughout the writings medicine is spoken of as an art, and one thesis is entitled "The Art." The fine arrogance of this claim is better realized when we remember that in the Platonic philosophy art (*tekne*) is held almost in contempt beside the altitudes reached by the intellect unhampered by dull fact. In one of the later books its warm humanity is emphasized in the phrase "Where there is love of man, there is also love of the Art."

If the disease be of longer standing than three days when the face has these characteristics, go on to make the same inquiries as I ordered in the previous case, and also examine the other symptoms, both of the body generally and those of the eyes. For if they shun the light, or weep involuntarily, or are distorted, or if one becomes less than the other, if the whites be red or livid or have black veins in them, should rheum appear around the eyeballs, should they be restless or protruding or very sunken, or if the complexion of the whole face be changed—all these symptoms must be considered bad, in fact fatal.

You must also examine the partial appearance of the eyes in sleep. For if a part of the white appear when the lids are closed, should the cause not be diarrhoea or purging, or should the patient not be in the habit of so sleeping, it is an unfavourable, in fact a very deadly symptom. But if, along with one of the other symptoms, eyelid, lip or nose be bent or livid, you must know that death is close at hand. It is also a deadly sign when the lips are loose, hanging, cold and very white.

These paragraphs (the book runs to twenty-five in all) bring out two important features—the accurate noting of details, the recognition of the essential with the exclusion of all irrelevancies, and the importance attached to knowledge of the course of the disease. This wish to know the future was a strong characteristic of the Greek mind which, in all aspects of doubt, turned to oracle, divination or augury. It is curious, as most commentators have remarked, that prognosis is considered to be so much more important than diagnosis. Diseases are named but not classified and acute diseases are the writer's chief concern. In the astonishing series of clinical histories included in the *Epidemics* (but in fact illustrating the thesis on *Prognostic*) we find no diagnosis such as, according to Hippocrates' complaint, was carried to extremes by the physicians of Cnidus. This concern with the future of an illness is no mere matter of prophecy, however. It includes the whole natural history of the disease and its relation to the human organism, which is a fundamental part of medicine. Without this knowledge treatment is arbitrary. "Just as the revival of Hippocratic observation in the seventeenth century gave a new birth to clinical medicine so the revival of Hippocratic prognosis in our own days . . . had no small share in bringing about the more modern revolutions in medical practice."—(*Withington*.)

The essential simplicity of Hippocratic treatment and its unpretentious nature, its utter lack of diagnostic boasting or loud promises of cure—such as brought so much of the craft to disrepute in Plato's day and disfigured in later centuries the

PLATE XVII

VOTIVE RELIEFS IN HONOUR OF ASKLEPIOS

These reliefs represent the faith-healing aspect of early Greek medicine. In the one above a sick man's litter has stopped by a tree, on which hangs the sacred snake. In that below, the snake is seen beneath the throne on which the god sits. By his side stands Hygieia, his daughter, the goddess of health. In front are two suppliants.

Ny Carlsberg and Athens National Museums: photos, Mansell and Alinari.

PLATE XVII

PLATE XVIII

PLATE XVIII

PERSISTENCE OF THE SACRED SERPENT OF HEALING

As long as the recorded history of medicine is the association with it of the serpent of healing. It is clearly seen in the Sumerian vase (left) which dates from 2350 B.C., and was dedicated by Gudea of Babylon to Ningishzida, son of Ninazu, the Master Physician. It is always associated with Asklepian monuments (*see* Plate XVII).

The same serpent is recognisable in the existing species (right), *Coluber longissimus* (*Æsculapius*). The species was named after Asklepios by Aldrovandi of Bologna (1522–1605), and has generally been regarded as the true serpent of Asklepios. It is found in various parts of Europe. It remains the emblem of the art of healing and is found in many official badges and seals, including that of the Royal Army Medical Corps.

PLATE XVIII.

PERSISTENCE OF THE SACRED SERPENT OF HEALING

As long as the recorded history of medicine is the association with it of the serpent of healing. It is clearly seen in the Sumerian vase (left) which dates from 2350 B.C., and was dedicated by Gudea of Babylon to Ningishzida, son of Ninazu, the Master Physician. It is always associated with Asklepian monuments (see Plate XVII). The same serpent is recognisable in the existing species (right), Coluber longissima (Æsculapius). The species was named after Asklepios by Aldrovandi of Bologna (1522-1605), and has generally been regarded as the true serpent of Asklepios. It is found in various parts of Europe. It remains the emblem of the art of healing and is found in many official badges and seals, including that of the Royal Army Medical Corps.

Copyright, Wellcome Historical Medical Museum.

work of men of real greatness—are well seen in the next two works on our list, the *Regimen in Acute Diseases* and the *Epidemics*.

In these two books we also have a fairly complete statement of the Greek knowledge of diseases, their recognition and their treatment. It is beyond question a marvellous achievement. Mr. Jones considers the *Epidemics* to be "the most remarkable product of Greek science."

From the *Regimen* we learn that the mild treatment included but a few drugs—hellebore and other simple purges and herbal drinks made from raisins, wheat, saffron, pomegranates "and so forth." Its mainstay appears to be barley gruel and barley water with hydromel (honey and water) as a soothing drink and oxymel (honey and vinegar) as an expectorant. Detailed instructions are given for the preparation of the gruel and long discussions of its effects. Ordinary water is considered to be definitely harmful. No other form of nourishment is mentioned in these cases although dietetics played an extremely important part in the Hippocratic method. Other therapeutic measures recommended in *Acute Diseases* (which appear to be mainly confined to chest complaints) are baths (with affusions, sponging, scraping, rubbing) wet and dry fomentations, bran poultices, enemata and suppositories, for all of which careful directions are given.

From this work and the greater work the *Epidemics* we learn the main diseases with which the Greek physician had to grapple. Many of them carry to-day the names he gave them. Malaria in all forms was the greatest foe. Symptoms and consequences of the mild and malignant fevers and of the intermittent forms are vividly and accurately described. One of its consequences, mental and physical prostration, was named melancholia (*melagkolia*). Among other diseases whose names are Greek in origin (transliterated here) were diarrhoea (*diarroia*), dysentery (*dusenteria*), pleurisy (*pleuritis*), pneumonia (*peripneumonia*), consumption (*phthisis*), ophthalmia (*ophthalmia*).

Something must be said of the principal doctrines inculcated in these works. They are four—coction, crisis, the critical days and the natural healing power. In the background were the humours (propounded by the earlier Pythagorean school as we have seen) whose harmony was health, and whose disturbance was disease, the most important here being bile and phlegm. The working theory, the practical man's guide, was provided by the four doctrines. The first is difficult for the modern mind to appreciate. Coction (*pepsis*) is the process tending to recovery which gradually restores and perfects the equilibrium of the humours. This restoration was due, according to the fourth doctrine, to the powers of nature (the famous *vis medicatrix naturæ*) aided to the limit of the physician's powers by removing disturbing factors, including incorrect diet, as far as possible without active interference. That natural restoration was made by coction and the day it occurred or definitely failed was the day of crisis (*krisis*). Recovery or death followed. If the crisis was favourable the signs of coction were to be seen in the evacuation, through the usual excretory channels, of the residue of the humours after equilibrium was restored.

If normal evacuation by mouth, rectum, urethra or skin pore, failed the morbid residue might be concentrated at one point and an eruption, tumour or even gangrene might result. This, called *apostasis*, is ingeniously translated by Mr. Jones as "an abscession."

The third doctrine, the law of critical days, was perhaps in part a survival of the Pythagorean ideas of mystic numbers but more probably was associated with the periodical variations of malaria which, as has been noted, was the principal disease.

The fourth doctrine, with its associated expectant form of treatment, seems to us so obvious as to require no comment. Actually it is one of that great collection of splendid platitudes which make Greek ideas seem so obvious and simple to unhistorical and imperceptive minds and prove on examination to be fundamental and original contributions to human thought.

> We live some twenty-three centuries later than Hippocrates; for some sixteen of those centuries the civilized world thought that to retain health periodical bleedings and potions were necessary; for the last century or two we have been gradually returning on the Hippocratic position.—(*Charles Singer*, " The Legacy of Greece ".)

The great *Epidemics*, books I and III, which though numbered thus in all the MSS., are really continuous, are genuinely Hippocratic.

Their associated clinical histories, bedside notes of cases written with utter sincerity, devoid of any form or sign of self interest or care for anything but untainted scientific truth, are the only records of their kind for over eighteen hundred years and would not easily be improved upon as models even in these modern days.

The book is in two somewhat disconnected parts. One, traditionally called " Constitutions " consists of descriptions of climatic conditions of definite type associated in the writer's view with the spread of disease of epidemic type. (It is amusing to note in passing that the weather described in these reports includes specimens of a kind familiar to modern ears—Winter was northerly; many violent and abundant rains; . . . there were fine intervals!) The other is a series of histories of acute diseases of specific individuals and has but little connection with the first part as has already been noted.

The most important diseases discussed in the Constitutions, which the writer considers to be epidemic are consumption and the various forms of malaria. The following general description of the former disease and its victims, taken from *Epidemics* III, displays a very high standard of accuracy and practical medical knowledge:

> The severest and most troublesome disease, as well as the most fatal, was the consumption. Many cases began in the winter, and of these several took to their bed, though some went about ailing without doing so. Early in the spring most of those who had gone to bed died, while none of the others lost their cough, though it became easier in the summer.
>
> During autumn all took to bed and many died. Most of these were ill for a long time. Now most of these began suddenly to grow worse, showing the following symptoms: frequent shivering; often continuous and acute fever; unseasonable, copious, cold sweats throughout; great chill with difficult recovery of heat; bowels variously constipated, then quickly relaxing, and violently relaxing in all cases near the end; the humours about the lungs spread downwards; abundance of unfavourable urine; malignant wasting.
>
> The coughs throughout were frequent, bringing up copious, concocted and liquid sputa, but without much pain; but even if there was pain, in all cases the purging from the lungs took place very mildly. The throat did not smart very much, nor did salt humours cause any distress at all. The fluxes, however, viscid, white, moist, frothy, which came from the head, were abundant. But by far the worst symptom that attended both these cases and the others was the distaste for food, as has been mentioned. They had no relish either for drink with nourishment, but they remained entirely without thirst. Heaviness in the body. Coma. In most of them there was swelling, which developed into dropsy. Shivering fits and delirium near death.
>
> The physical characteristics of the consumptives were:—skin smooth, whitish, lentil-coloured, reddish; bright eyes; a leuco-phlegmatic condition; shoulder-blades projecting like wings. Women too so. As to those with a melancholic or a rather sanguine complexion, they were attacked by ardent fevers, phrenitis and dysenteric troubles. Tenesmus affected young, phlegmatic people; the chronic diarrhoea and acrid, greasy stools affected persons of a bilious temperament.

A most interesting point in the last paragraph of this quotation is that here we see reasonably and sanely applied that doctrine of the humours which, as we have noted, became in other hands a sterilizing influence during seventeen hundred years of medicine. In Hippocratic medicine it is at least similar in nature to the modern study of individual temperaments and constitutions.

Malaria is described with equal accuracy and attention to relevant detail. Following several pages of similarly important character we have a paragraph of the highest significance which not only illustrates the application of the doctrines of crisis, coction and "abscession" referred to above, but lays down in a few pregnant sentences the whole duty of the physician:

> In all dangerous cases you should be on the watch for all favourable coctions of the evacuations from all parts, or for fair and critical abscessions. Coctions signify nearness of crisis and sure recovery of health, but crude and unconcocted evacuations, which change into bad abcessions, denote absence of crisis, pain, prolonged illness, death or a return of the same symptoms. But it is by a consideration of other signs that one must decide which of these results will be most likely. Declare the past, diagnose the present, foretell the future; practise these acts. As to diseases, make a habit of two things—to help, or at least to do no harm. The art has three factors, the disease, the patient, the physician. The physician is the servant of the art. The patient must co-operate with the physician in combating the disease.

We turn to the incomparable clinical histories. It has often been remarked that in his attachment to the purely relevant parts of the case under observation and the total exclusion of all irrelevancies the physician, in recording these observations is no longer healer but the detached scientist. He does not consider the cure and shows no emotion in recording, as he does in twenty-five cases out of forty-two, that the patient dies.

Where all are of outstanding interest and historical importance selection is difficult but the following three cases must suffice:

> Chærion, who lay sick in the house of Demænetus, was seized with fever after drinking. At once there was painful heaviness of the head; no sleep; bowels disturbed with thin, rather bilious stools.
>
> *Third day.* Acute fever, trembling of the head, particularly of the lower lip; after a while rigor, convulsions, complete delirium; an uncomfortable night.
>
> *Fourth day.* Quiet; snatches of sleep; wandering.
>
> *Fifth day.* Pain; general exacerbation; irrational talk; uncomfortable night; no sleep.

Sixth day. The same symptoms.

Seventh day. Rigor; acute fever; sweating all over; crisis.

This patient's stools were throughout bilious, scanty and uncompounded. Urine thin, not of a good colour, with a cloudy substance floating in it. About the eighth day the urine had a better colour, with a slight, white sediment; quite rational and no fever; an intermission.

Ninth day. Relapse. About the fourteenth day acute fever.

Sixteenth day. Vomited bilious, yellow matters rather frequently.

Seventeenth day. Rigor; acute fever; sweating; crisis ended the fever.

Urine after relapse and crisis of a good colour, with a sediment; no delirium during the relapse.

Eighteenth day. Slight heat; rather thirsty; urine thin, with cloudy substance floating in it; slight delirium.

Nineteenth day. No fever; pain in the neck; sediment in urine.

Twentieth day. Complete crisis.

Could anything be more modern in feeling, i.e. permanently true in tone and character, than this and the following set of calmly observed bedside records? Note in the first excerpt from this twenty-five-century old case-book the double crisis and final recovery.

In Thasos Pythion, who lay sick above the shrine of Heracles, after labour, fatigue and careless living, was seized by violent rigor and acute fever. Tongue dry; thirst; bilious; no sleep; urine rather black, with a substance suspended in it, which formed no sediment.

Second day. About mid-day chill in the extremities, especially in the hands and head; could not speak or utter a sound; respiration short for a long time; recovered warmth; thirst; a quiet night; slight sweats about the head.

Third day. A quiet day, but later, about sunset, grew rather chilly; nausea; distress; painful night without sleep; small, solid stools were passed.

Fourth day. Early morning peaceful, but about mid-day all symptoms were exacerbated; chill; speechless and voiceless; grew worse; recovered warmth after a time; black urine with a substance floating in it; night peaceful; slept.

Fifth day. Seemed to be relieved, but there was heaviness in the bowels with pain; thirst; painful night.

Sixth day. Early morning peaceful; towards evening the pains were greater; exacerbation; but later a little clyster caused a good movement of the bowels. Slept at night.

Seventh day. Nausea; rather uneasy; urine oily; much distress at night; wandering; no sleep at all.

Eighth day. Early in the morning snatches of sleep; but quickly there was chill; loss of speech; respiration thin and weak; in the evening he recovered warmth again; was delirious; towards morning slightly better; stools uncompounded, small, bilious.

Ninth day. Comatose; nausea whenever he woke up. Not over thirsty. About sunset was uncomfortable; wandered; a bad night.

Tenth day. In the early morning was speechless; great chill; acute fever; much sweat; death.

In this case the pains on even days.

The distress spoken of in the above case was probably abdominal. The fever ran a rapid course and was intermittent with recurring severe exhaustion. In the third example the fever ran for three weeks and for the greater part of the time the patient was delirious or unconscious. The description is particularly vivid. For a comment on the obvious intervals between visits see below.

In Thasos the wife of Delearces, who lay sick on the plain, was seized after a grief with an acute fever with shivering. From the beginning she would wrap herself up, and throughout, without speaking a word, she would fumble, pluck, scratch, pick hairs, weep and then laugh, but she did not sleep; though stimulated the bowels passed nothing. She drank a little when the attendants suggested it. Urine thin and scanty; fever slight to the touch; coldness of the extremities.

Ninth day. Much wandering followed by return of reason; silent.

Fourteenth day. Respiration rare and large with long intervals, becoming afterwards short.

Seventeenth day. Bowels under a stimulus passed disordered matters, then her very drink passed unchanged; nothing coagulated. The patient noticed nothing; the skin tense and dry.

Twentieth day. Much rambling followed by recovery of reason; speechless; respiration short.

Twenty-first day. Death.

The respiration of this patient throughout was rare and large; took no notice of anything; she constantly wrapped herself up; either much rambling or silence throughout.

Note the absence of all diagnosis and of treatment beyond purging. It has been one of the occupations of medical writers in all times to supply the missing diagnosis. These three examples from the forty-two are given to support and illustrate the claims made earlier for the supremacy of this department of Hippocratic medicine.

The only other comment that seems to be required is the mention of "attendants". This, as Mr. Jones has noted, is with the exception of a later book, *Decorum*, not included in the Canon, the only indication of a Greek system of nursing. Obviously the physician must have had some of the many daily observations reported to him, and if the attendants were not trained nurses they must have had some medical knowledge. The passage from *Decorum* referred to gives the clue.

> Let one of your pupils be left in charge, to carry out instructions without unpleasantness, and to administer the treatment. Choose out those who have been already admitted into the mysteries of the art, so as to add anything necessary, and to give treatment with safety. He is there also to prevent those things escaping notice in the intervals between visits. Never put a layman in charge of anything, otherwise if a mischance occur the blame will fall on you. Let there never be any doubt about the points which will secure the success of your plans, and no blame will attach to you, but achievement will bring you pride. So say beforehand all this at the time the things are done, to those whose business it is to have fuller knowledge.

This book gives us several sidelights of historical value of Greek medicine. One of the more humanly amusing indicates a difficulty which is not unknown to the modern general practitioner.

> Keep a watch also on the faults of the patients, which often make them lie about the taking of things prescribed. For through not taking disagreeable drinks, purgative or other, they sometimes die. What they have done never results in a confession, but the blame is thrown upon the physician.

The magnificent *Aphorisms*, which are next upon our list, are written in a style which was adapted by the medical schools from the philosophers for the advantages of its pithy, striking form and its aid to the memory. The *Sentences* of Cnidus, already referred to, were in this form. If the philosophic aphorism was tinged with poesy, the medical was a clear generalization of observed fact, as the examples (from Mr. W. H. S. Jones' new translation) which follow will show. The total number of the *Aphorisms* is four hundred and twelve.

From the First Section.

XIII.   Old men endure fasting most easily, then men of middle age, youths very badly, and worst of all children, especially those of a liveliness greater than the ordinary.

XX. Do not disturb a patient either during or just after a crisis, and try no experiments, neither with purges nor with other irritants, but leave him alone.

From the Second Section.

II. When sleep puts an end to delirium it is a good sign.

V. Spontaneous weariness indicates disease.

VI. Those who, suffering from a painful affection of the body, for the most part are unconscious of the pains, are disordered in mind.

XXXI. When a convalescent has a good appetite without improving his bodily condition it is a bad sign.

XXXVIII. Food or drink which, though slightly inferior, is more palatable, is preferable to that which is superior but less palatable.

XXXIX. Old men generally have less illness than young men, but such complaints as become chronic in old men generally last until death.

XLIV. Those who are constitutionally very fat are more apt to die quickly [have less power to resist severe disease than those who are thin].

From the Third Section.

IX. It is in autumn that diseases are most acute and, in general, most deadly; spring is most healthy and least deadly.

XIV. All diseases occur at all seasons, but some diseases are more apt to occur and to be aggravated at certain seasons.

XVIII. As for the seasons, in spring and early summer children and young people enjoy the greatest well-being and good health; in summer and part of autumn, the aged; for the remainder of autumn and in winter, the middle-aged.

From the Fourth Section.

XXIV. A dysentery beginning with black bile is mortal.

XXXVII. Cold sweats, occurring with high fever, indicate death; with a milder fever they indicate a protracted disease.

LXVI. In acute fevers, convulsions and violent pains in the bowels are a bad sign.

LXXIX. When the urine contains a sandy sediment there is a stone in the bladder.

From the Fifth Section.

II. A convulsion supervening upon a wound is deadly [i.e. tetanus].

III. Convulsion or hiccough, supervening on a copious flux of blood, is a bad sign.

PLATE XIX
THE GREEK IDEA OF THE IDEAL PHYSICIAN

There is no authentic portrait of Hippocrates, but in many grave-featured busts of the Father of Medicine a more or less common ideal is traceable, due perhaps to the profound impression made by Hippocrates upon his contemporaries. This fine bust is Greek work of the 3rd or 2nd century B.C.

British Museum.

PLATE XIX

PLATE XX

IX. Consumption occurs chiefly between the ages of eighteen and thirty-five.

XIII. When patients spit up frothy blood, the discharge comes from the lungs.

From the Sixth Section.

VI. Kidney troubles, and affections of the bladder, are cured with difficulty when the patient is aged.

LI. Those who when in health are suddenly seized with pains in the head, becoming forthwith dumb and breathing stertorously, die within seven days unless fever comes on. [Apoplectic seizure.]

LIV. In acute affections attended with fever, moaning respiration is a bad sign.

From the Seventh Section.

I. In acute diseases chill of the extremities is a bad sign.

XI. Pneumonia supervening on pleurisy is bad. [Alternative reading: Pneumonia often supervenes on pleurisy.]

LVIII. In cases of concussion of the brain from any cause, the patients, of necessity, lose at once the power of speech.

LXVI. If you give to a fever patient the same food as you would to a healthy person, it is strength to the healthy but disease to the sick.

LXXXIII. When in illnesses tears flow voluntarily from the eyes, it is a good sign, when involuntarily a bad sign.

It would be an insult to the reader's intelligence to do more than emphasize the ever-living sanity and what we, somewhat impertinently, call modernity, of these notes from the Master Physician's case books.

The two remaining books of the Hippocratic Canon need only to be referred to briefly. We have noted that *Airs, Waters, Places* is the first book ever written on climatology and the hygiene of places. Greek physicians were travellers and a book like this would give them valuable information concerning medical conditions of a strange town and the type of disease likely to be met with there. This purpose is clearly stated in the opening paragraphs of the book:

> Whoever wishes to pursue properly the science of medicine must proceed thus. First he ought to consider what effects each season of the year can produce; for the seasons are not at all alike, but differ widely both in themselves and in their changes.
>
> The next point is the hot winds and the cold, especially those that are universal, but also those that are peculiar to each particular region.

F

Dioscorides, Soranus, Galen, were students. Its Great Library, a genuine wonder of the ancient world (there was a daughter library at the temple of Serapis), contained in 50 B.C., it is said, about 700,000 rolls of MSS. (many of them doubtless being replicas), including, without doubt, hundreds of masterpieces of classical antiquity, all now lost. Its precise fate is not known, but there is little doubt that neglect, repeated religious riots and the accidents of war resulted in its disappearance before the fourth century A.D.

Among the greater names in Alexandrian medicine were the anatomists Hierophilus and Erasistratus. Modern anatomy practically dates from the Alexandrians, but we cannot go into the details of their achievements. Of interest to our thesis are certain medical facts. Pliny says that Hierophilus was the first physician who searched into the causes of disease, and Pliny is so prejudiced a witness in the matter of Greek medicine that this may be taken as high testimony. Certainly Hierophilus was an acknowledged Hippocratist, a humorist, and he is said to have declared that the best physician was he who was able to distinguish between the possible and the impossible. He counted the pulse by the water-clock, and studied its rate and rhythm.

Erasistratus, whom Galen contemned so bitterly, wrote on the importance of hygiene in the prevention of disease and contrived a system which, rejecting the humours, filled the arteries with air or vital spirits and the veins with blood. This idea that the arteries contained air persisted for many centuries and was an important obstacle to the discovery of the circulation of the blood. Plethora of the veins was the general cause of inflammation, fever and disease. He disapproved, however, of bleeding (venesection) and his medicine consisted of mild laxatives, barley-water and wine in extremely small doses.

Hellenic medical culture in Alexandria was in general highly developed. Dietetics, materia medica, pathology, public baths, regulations for wet nursing, circumcision and embalming are all described in some detail in the great Oxyrhynchus papyrii which has been studied by Sudhoff. This culture, and the schools that developed from it, was, after Hippocrates himself, the main influence in medical development of the next five or six centuries, particularly in Rome, to which we now turn.

Actual Roman medicine was from the beginning up to the arrival of the despised Greeks in the second century B.C. a negligible affair. Of genuine Roman medicine there was at no

PLATE XXI
GREEK PHYSICIANS AND THEIR PATIENTS

Few representations of ancient Greek physicians have survived. The upper example, enlarged in plaster from an intaglio gem, dating about 350 B.C., shows the physician examining his patient. The second example is particularly interesting: its inscription states that it is a funerary monument of "Jason, also called Dekmos, the Acharnian, a physician": it comes from Athens and dates from the second century A.D. Its somewhat late date probably accounts for its slightly crude sculpture, since Greek funerary stelæ are generally distinguished by their great beauty. As Dr. Charles Singer has pointed out, the physician is feeling, or palpating, the liver of his patient, a dwarfish man, whose condition suggests that described in one of the "Aphorisms" of Hippocrates, where he says that "in jaundice it is serious if the liver becomes hardened". Such a condition can be detected by touch.

Wellcome Historical Medical Museum and British Museum.

PLATE XXI

PLATE XXII

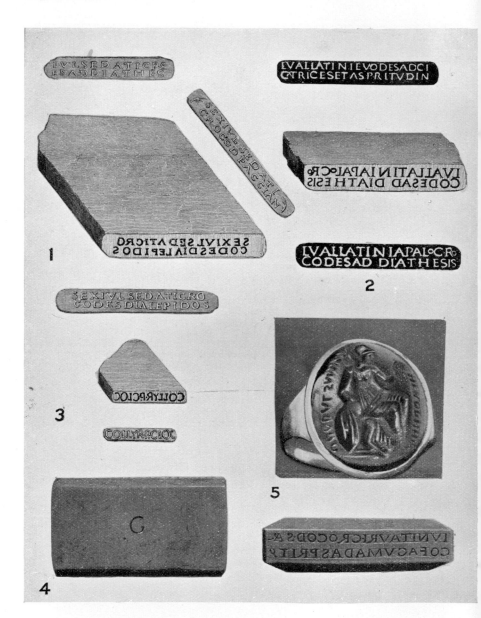

PLATE XXII

How the Oculist Quacks of Rome Stamped their Eye Salves

Large numbers of stamps with inscriptions in slate or steatite have been found on Roman sites in Europe. The engraved examples, 1–3 (from Sir James Young Simpson), are British. A photograph of another British example is seen below (4).

The inscriptions on the edges of the stamps gave the name of the oculist, his specific and its purpose, often in the nature of a puff. The inscription at the top of No. 2 may be translated as "the evodes of Lucius Vallantinus for cicatrices and granulations". The lower edge of the same stamp was used for his "mild crocodes for eye affections". Evodes, according to Scribonius Largus, was a complicated preparation including copper, myrrh, opium and other ingredients.

These eye salves were sold in solid form to be dissolved in water and applied with a probe. The ring (5) was used for sealing packets of eye-salves: its gem is engraved with the figure of Athena and the title "Balsam of Herophilus", probably an obscure oculist of the first century B.C.

British Museum.

time anything of any account. That which was of substance was Greek or Græco-Roman. The Roman religious system forbade any scientific medicine. The early Latin, and even the later Roman of Republic and Empire, with his tinge of Etruscan gloom, was a hard headed yet superstitious person imbued with a complicated folk-lore. Every disease, every symptom in those early Latin times, had its minor deity, and these mainly malevolent spirits and powers had to be placated in a businesslike way. The chief of the family, the pater-familias, supreme in his household, was his own physician, and there was no occasion for an external doctor. He kept a few simple herbal drugs in the store cupboard, the Penates, and these, with what amounted to magic, sufficed. "Up to the time of Cato," says Sir Clifford Allbutt, "the folk method was theurgy plus the drug."

Cato, the consul and censor (234–149 B.C.), was himself an excellent example of this type. He objected strongly to the Greek physic with which he was acquainted—probably nothing better than that of medical adventurers and charlatans—and maintained the health of his family and the slaves on his estates mainly by prescribing cabbage in various forms, wine and magic sentences. As Sir Clifford Allbutt in his lectures on Roman medicine remarks, the cabbage probably had virtue as an antiscorbutic in the absence of fresh meat in winter. Other prescriptions which he used appear to have come from a traditional book of recipes of which something is known from Pliny's *Natural History*. "Many were futile, many were filthy."

So Rome had no science, and, if the diatribes of Pliny are to be trusted, the older type of Roman, like Cato the austere Republican, objected vehemently to the introduction of Greek science, particularly Greek medicine. The first Greek doctors were slaves employed to treat gladiators and gymnasts and were generally mistrusted. In the second century B.C. Greek ideas began to be more readily absorbed in Rome.

Late in the first century B.C., however, we find Asclepiades of Bithynia a successful and fashionable physician in Rome, a man of culture who became the friend of Cicero. He therefore had the honour of effectively introducing Greek medicine to Rome (he went there about 90 B.C.). It is unfortunate that he did not introduce the Hippocratic doctrines. He is reported to have described the method of Hippocrates as "a meditation upon death," and that so far from curing Nature did as much cure'). Galen thought so little of these gentry that he considered it useless to write of eye diseases scientifically for, he said, the oculists would not understand him. Oculists of the better class held official and military appointments, one even, as Withington notes, being styled "Oculist to the British Navy!" —an appointment to the Roman fleet in British waters.

So the stage is set for the entry of the last great figure in the medicine of antiquity—Claudius Galen, whose name means "the peaceable," but whose life was noisy strife, who before he was twenty-one had written a text book for midwives, a book on eye diseases, three on the lungs and a polemic; who, though he was inferior to his master Hippocrates, knew all that his world had of knowledge; who wrote five hundred lengthy treatises on every subject, and by his systemization of medicine, anatomy, physiology and disease gave to the world "the law" in these departments which none gainsaid effectively for twelve hundred years. If he ended, as he did, by becoming the dead hand in medicine of medieval times that was due to medieval mentality rather than to the doctrines of this "bonny fighter."

Born in A.D. 131 at Pergamos, in Asia Minor, a medical centre of renown with a library only second to Alexandria, Galen studied the chief philosophies of his day, and at seventeen turned to medicine, both his philosophical and his medical studies being eclectic in the general and better sense of the term. In A.D. 162 he arrives in busy, factious, Rome. Antoninus Pius died the year before. Marcus Aurelius is emperor.

There he finds active the four principal schools of medicine whose doctrines we have noted earlier; active in practice and in propaganda of their doctrines, the commonest method being vicious backbiting and strident abuse of rivals. The calm detached Hippocratic atmosphere with its dignified professional ethic is lost. Even Galen, brilliant figure though he be as practitioner and anatomist, is no exception. At no time does he attempt to conceal his contempt for his colleagues or the leaders of the sects. For instance, in one of his best works, *On the Natural Faculties*, after refuting to his complete satisfaction the atomistic doctrines of Epicurus (the great Stoic philosopher) and Asclepiades (the physician) he begins a fresh chapter thus:

> We have talked sufficient nonsense not willingly but because we were forced, as the proverb says, " to behave madly among madmen." . . . Let us forget the absurdities of Asclepiades.

PLATE XXIII

THE ROMAN PHYSICIAN

The relief, from a sarcophagus found in Rome, and dating from about A.D. 100, shows a Græco-Roman physician at his desk. He reads a MS. taken from a cabinet, on top of which is a case of surgical instruments. For a discussion of the relief see Petersen, König, Deutsch. Archaeol, Inst., Rome, 1900, Band 15.

Copyright, Wellcome Historical Medical Museum.

The metal drug case below is divided into separate compartments each with its cover and a sliding lid over the whole. It is of the second or third century A.D. and came from Asia Minor. Other examples of Roman physicians' outfits of this date have also been discovered in Asia Minor.

British Museum.

PLATE XXIII

PLATE XXIV

PLATE XXIV
MONUMENTS OF ROMAN PUBLIC HYGIENE

In the absence of cheap and reliable metal for pipes, the expert water engineers of Rome fell back upon the plentiful stone and other similar local materials with which they constructed their aqueducts, many of which still exist. The upper example, at Tunis, was built by Hadrian to bring water to Carthage from the mountains. The Aqua Claudia (below) was one of the nine which supplied Rome in Hadrian's day, seven of which were constructed before it was built in A.D. 38. It brought water from the springs of Tivoli and stretched, as the photograph shows, far across the Campagna. On top of it a row of brick arches, the remains of which can still be seen, carried yet another aqueduct, the Anio Novus, which was the ninth. Two more aqueducts were built in later reigns, and the total supply is estimated at about forty million gallons per day. The poor fetched their supply from the public fountains while the wealthy had it brought to their houses in lead pipes (*see* next Plate) stamped with their names. It is estimated the supply averaged about forty gallons per person, but this included the vast bathing establishments.

From " Wonders of the Past," Amalgamated Press, Ltd.

Again when he is discussing the Hippocratic view of the functions of the kidneys he cannot, he says, keep silence.

> For I know that if one passes over the Hippocratic view and makes some other pronouncement . . . one cannot fail to make oneself ridiculous. It was for this reason that Erasistratus kept silence and Asclepiades lied; they are like slaves who have had plenty to say in the early part of their career and have managed by excessive rascality to escape frequent accusations, but who, later, when caught in the act of thieving, cannot find any excuse.—
> (*Dr. A. J. Brock's translations.*)

And he really had (and showed elsewhere) genuine respect for both these men; he but reflects the spirit and tone of his day. Nevertheless he knew the limitations of the party man. Speaking of the disputations of "our present-day Asclepiadeans" he remarks:

> So difficult an evil to get rid of is this sectarian partisanship, so excessively resistant to all cleansing processes, harder to heal than any itch!

Let us turn to his actual and lasting merits.

Of the five hundred treatises one hundred and eighty-one have survived, of which about one hundred are accepted as genuine. Many of his medical works were destroyed, as he tells us, in a fire about ten years before his death which consumed his *Apotheke* (drug-store) on the Sacred Way. In sheer volume of writing he leads the ancient world, and though its literary quality is unequal, many of his treatises being written in highly polished Greek and others but outlines never filled in, he presents, in a system which he intended to be universal, a complete synthesis of Greek and Græco-Roman medicine and allied sciences. He was much more than a compiler or systematizer, however, as his clever experimental work in anatomy and physiology showed. His medicine and pathology were based on the Hippocratic humours, and his own theory of the temperaments and worked up by arrangement of all the possible combinations into a system which—on paper—was finely logical. "No phenomenon was without a name, no problem without a solution."—(*Allbutt.*) Later ages accepted it only too completely. Its authority was not to be challenged, the inspiration of its written word a matter of dogma and its interpretation and application to unfortunate patients but a question of dialectic.

theory which is, in effect, entirely modern, dividing the causes of disease into three—exciting, predisposing, and immediate. This recognition of predisposition to disease as shown by temperament and physical constitution was a pathological advance of great importance. The morbid processes as a whole are grouped as diathesis. Symptoms are "morbid affections dependent and necessarily following upon diseases, as the shadow follows the substance."

In his therapeutics Galen's doctrines and practice are a curious mixture of the sensible and the extravagant. In spite of his duty paid at the Hippocratic shrine he propounded and practised much that interfered with the course of Nature. "Though he did treat fevers by tepid baths, he was heavily pharmaceutical; too disposed to forget his physiological and pathological methods in a search for specifics and thus to accumulate recipe medicine." —(*Allbutt*.) Undoubtedly he added extravagantly to the number of drugs already in use and did not disguise that he was, to some extent, satisfying the popular demand for "something in a bottle" (*Populus remedia cupit*). Later writers dubbed him the Father of Pharmacy (whence "galenicals"), but in this department he was largely a compiler. Certainly the influence of his materia medica was great and long lasting.

The sensible aspect is well displayed in the doctrine of the indications—"whatever enables us to draw conclusions concerning treatment apart from experience." From this we still have the special medical use of the word "indicate"—to suggest or call for a particular form of treatment. The main Galenic indications for treatment are:

(1) *indicatio morbi*, dependent upon character, type, and intensity of the disease;
(2) *indicatio symptomatica*, demanding treatment by lessening pain, regulating evacuations, etc., by contrary, if against Nature, and by similar if in accordance with Nature;
(3) *indicatio vitalis*, dangerous condition to be averted.

To these were added indications or contra-indications from the patient himself—temperament, age, strength, residence—from the season, the atmosphere and—an Asklepian echo—the patient's dreams.

Finally, it may be said that as a therapeutist he paid close attention to dietetics, gymnastics, massage, and the use of baths in great variety—water, sun, sand, minerals and herbs all being employed in his balneo-therapy.

It is not appropriate to our scheme to discuss the excellent

PLATE XXV
Roman Achievement in Drains and Plumbing

In both these matters the modern world has not greatly surpassed Roman methods. The lead water-pipes (note the remains of a wiped joint) were found under the floor of the house of Livia on the Palatine Hill, Rome. The Cloaca Maxima, Rome's oldest and longest sewer, may well be, says Professor Bosanquet, the work of Etruscan engineers. It is a great paved and vaulted tunnel which runs past the Imperial Forums into the Tiber, a distance of, roughly, a mile. Its exit into the Tiber is seen in the photograph. The lower portion has never been out of order, but medieval neglect resulted in the upper stretches being choked until they were cleared in the late nineteenth century. At least two other great sewers existed, now buried deep beneath the modern city. Many other Roman cities had equally excellent sewers.

From " The Universal History of the World," Amalgamated Press, Ltd.; photos, Donald McLeish and Alinari.

PLATE XXV

PLATE XXVI

PLATE XXVI
Sanitation in a Roman Colonial City

The ruins of Timgad, which are one of the great tourist sights of N. Africa, include extremely well-ordered hygienic and sanitary installations. In addition to fifteen public bath establishments there were finely appointed public lavatories, a portion of one of which, placed near the Forum, is seen in the photograph. It had twenty-six carved stone seats, each enclosed by stone dolphins, and its drains were kept constantly flushed by a fountain in the centre. Timgad was laid out as a colony by Trajan early in the second century A.D.

From " Wonders of the Past," Amalgamated Press, Ltd.

anatomy (excellent though based on animal dissection) and interesting and highly important physiology of the last of the ancients, but one item in his physiology is worthy of note, since it concerns a subject to which we shall return in the seventeenth century. The quotation is taken from Dr. E. T. Withington.

> In opposition to his predecessors he declared that respiration serves not only to cool the body but to maintain the animal heat and made the happy suggestion that when we discover what part of the atmosphere supports combustion we shall also know what is the source of the bodily temperature.

It is a remarkable fact that no one had sufficient vision to follow up this inspired guess until our own John Mayow (1645–79) recognized the existence of this substance concerned with combustion and respiration.

It was Galen's philosophy, partly derived from Aristotle, that not only won a way in his own time for his essentially scholastic system, but gained him pre-eminence in later ages. His attitude that every part of the body, every physiological process was designed by superior—divine—intelligence to serve its particular end was one which made it possible for medieval theology, whether Christian or Islamic, to accept and absorb his teachings. The philosophers call it teleology—the doctrine of final causes —but its classification is of less importance than the fact that it avoided the offence to orthodoxy which was offered by the pagan and more scientific Hippocrates.

Summing up, we may say in the words of the historian of Greek medicine in Rome:

> If in later ages Galen's really great qualities and important discoveries were enormously inflated, even to infallibility, yet after all he was the greatest master of the scientific method from the second century to Roger Bacon.

Before we leave the Roman world something must be said of the excellent system of hygiene and hospital for in this, as in the theory and practice of medicine, the Middle Ages register a catacysmal decline.

The primal hygienic need of great cities, water, was amazingly well served in Rome and the cities of the Empire. Fourteen great aqueducts, ten of which were built by A.D. 110, supplied the capital with some 40,000,000 gallons of drinking water daily (estimates vary widely, a conservative recent calculation giving 1,540,000 gallons for the four principal aqueducts). The supply was proportionately in excess of that provided by any modern city. Professor Bosanquet says that "it was not until

G

CHAPTER VII

A THOUSAND YEARS OF DARKNESS: EUROPE, A.D. 200–1200

WHERE the Barbarian came he made a wilderness; chaos and ruin were his sign marks, but it is not to be supposed that the mental and material gloom of the Dark Ages was any sudden occurrence. Goth and Visigoth did but destroy in two centuries or so what was already decaying and had the heroic efforts of Diocletian and his successors stemmed permanently, instead of temporarily, the invading floods the death of the Roman polity would probably have been but delayed. The growth of the seeds of corruption was already too evident before the first massed attacks of Goth and Alemanni in the third century on the western frontiers of the Empire.

In medicine, as we have already seen, the decline towards the final fall had begun. After Galen we meet none but compilers and quacks. Original thought makes no considerable appearance and only a few names stand out. Oribasius, physician to that Emperor Julian, called the Apostate, who so cherished pagan learning and religion, compiled his *Medical Collection* in seventy-two books which are mainly of value for the extracts they give of earlier works otherwise lost. He is the last medical writer of importance of the ancient world. Afterwards cast out by the Christian Emperor Valens he became a favoured physician of the Visigoths. Two compilers of the early Christian period may be noticed in this brief survey. The Byzantine Ætius quotes largely from Galen and Oribasius, and is notable for long and elaborate prescriptions with theologic directions amounting to superstition. His *Tetrabiblos* was written in Greek in the mid-sixth century. Paulus Ægineta produced another voluminous epitome about 660 which, says Daremberg, "is without originality and equally drawn for the greater part from Oribasius and Galen," though mention of the fact is characteristically omitted. His sixth book on surgery, however, was superior to the rest of his writings. All these authors were for some time credited with greater originality than is their due.

PLATE XXVII

PAGE FROM AN ANGLO-SAXON "LEECHDOM" OF THE ELEVENTH CENTURY

Most of the surviving Saxon Medical MSS. are Christianised versions of an immensely popular Latin original, the "Herbarium" of Apuleius Barbarus. This particular leaf, from a well-illuminated MS. (MS. Vitellius C. III, dating *c.* 1050), gives recipes for treating snake bites, quartan ague, deafness and stones in the bladder. It includes the inevitable worm (*see* Plates XXVIII and XXIX). The hole in the left-hand corner of the leaf was caused by fire in Sir Richard Cotton's library in 1731 where this and many another MS. of the greatest value were originally collected. The plant on the right is, according to the text, a "wort, which is named saxifrage and by another name sundcorn, is produced on Downs and in stony places". It "leadeth to health" when "stones wax in the bladder."

British Museum.

PLATE XXVII

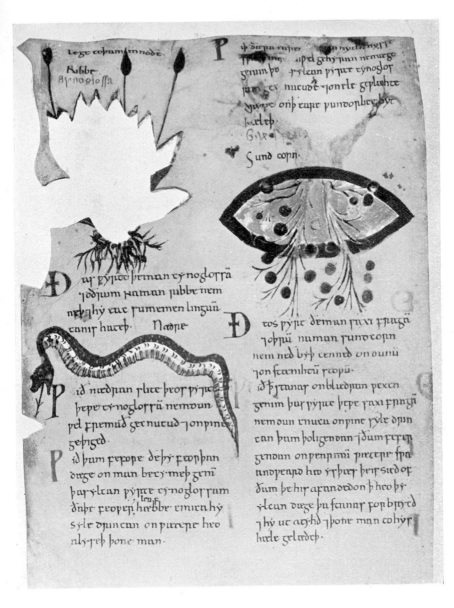

PLATE XXVIII

nac nos ipsi experti sumus. Ad uulña ꝫ Cancero mata. Herba Centaur̄
maior contrita ⁊ apposita. tumorem fieri non paciat̄. Ad suggillaciones ꝫ
liuores. Herbe centaurie suci puncti summe facit. Ad uulña recentia. Her
be centaurie puluis missus plagas conglutinat. ut etiam carnes coeresca̅t
⁊ centauria maior in aqua decocta. unde uuln̄ foueat̄. **N**omen herbe cen
tauria minor. Omoeos. Illebones. Pphe. Coa
beradeos. Egiptii
Amarach. Daci. Scir
sozila. Itali. febrifugia.
Alii. fel t̄re. Romani.
Amaritudo. Has herbas
duas chiam cirocentaurum
iuenisse ꝫ eas asclepio dedis
se. unde noīa centauria ac
ceperunt. Has̄cī locis solidis
ꝫ fortibus.

Ad uipere morsum. Herbe Centaurie minore contrita puluis er̄ aut̄

PLATE XXVIII
Herbal Magic in a Late Anglo-Saxon MS.

The twelfth century MS. of a Herbal (Harleian 5294), from which the drawings in this and the following Plate are taken, present characteristic ideas of the Dark Ages. It shows the fabled centaur, the man-headed horse, Chiron, who in Greek legend was first to discover the healing virtues of herbs. The centaur is offering a herb called centaury (but not the modern plant) to a physician. Below, the worm who appears largely in Teutonic notions of disease, flees from the magic herb.

British Museum.

Alexander of Tralles, a contemporary of Ætius at the court of Byzantium, may be quoted as an example of the way in which Greek medicine was finally submerged in superstition. He was a genuine eclectic, and his twelve books summarizing the Galenic pathology contain a refreshing amount of observation and judgement. The style is lofty and he recognizes the foolishness of treating the disease instead of the patient. Yet he gives the usual lengthy prescriptions and recommends charms and amulets of the most absurd description and variety. The following examples are taken from Withington:

> An amulet for quartan ague which I have proved by many experiments. Take a live dung beetle, put him in a red rag and hang him round the patient's neck.
>
> A green lizard together with the patient's nail parings may be used instead of the beetle.
>
> For epilepsy take a nail of a wrecked ship, make it into a bracelet and set therein the bone of a stag's heart taken from its body whilst alive; put it on the left arm; you will be astonished at the result.

So by the seventh century the last traces of active medicine have vanished, even in the home of Greek culture, Byzantium itself. Elsewhere it disappears much earlier. But half a century after Constantine had promulgated in 324 his famous Edict of toleration for all religions and "doxies" in the Empire, Theodosius decreed that paganism and Christianity could not exist side by side. Pagan rites were prohibited and pagan temples destroyed. Among them were inevitably the temples of Æsculapius where the incubation rites, described in an earlier page, were dangerously successful in their cures wrought in competition with the miracles effected by the saints and their relics. In Alexandria itself an archbishop in A.D. 391 led a crowd of fanatics to the destruction of the temple and library of Serapis. Everywhere throughout the Empire paganism saw its shrines broken up and their revenues confiscated; it bowed to the storm and conformed. It is a curious commentary that the votive offerings of limbs and diseased organs that had decorated the Æsculapian temples re-appeared dedicated in the churches and that the dream miracles of Saints Cosmas and Damian in the sixth and seventh centuries reflect closely the rites and usages of the "incubation" sleep of Æsculapius. According to the chroniclers of the miracles the two saints passed through the rows of patients sleeping in the church at Cyrrhos, where their bones were preserved, healing and giving advice for treatment.

In ancient Egypt magic killed both religion and science. Without stressing a parallel we find that medieval religion though not responsible for the initial decline of medicine—a decline which we have traced back to the century following Hippocrates himself—was yet a force which hastened the decline and would have completed its destruction had it not been for certain heretics and heathen.

From the early centuries of the Christian era we see the revival of those primitive theories of disease which have been discussed in earlier chapters. Basil, Bishop of Cæsarea A.D. 360, insists that disease may be caused by divine purpose or, by divine permission, by the agency of demons, and in such cases the physician is not to be called in, although the bishop himself declares medicine to be a noble profession.

A much more serious matter was an increasing restriction of freedom of thought and investigation. At the beginning and until the revival of thought which followed the beginning of the second millennium, the reasons are clear. "All medieval thought is characterized, nominally at least, by the conviction that each man has a soul to save, and that therefore salvation is the main end of every human being, not a distant ideal but the most practical duty," says Dr. Coulton, the learned medievalist. The Second Advent was never far beyond the horizon. "The world fabric might crash at any moment; what was the use of beginning a long chain of facts and inferences? . . . The painful lack of historical sense and of scientific observation or experiment during this long period" was partly due "to this predominantly other-worldly attitude of mind among many of the greatest thinkers." A consequence of this attitude is the concentration of intellectual effort upon theological controversy. Beginning with the speculation of the Greeks the habit of dialectic increased until in these troubled times it excludes all other thought and ranges from such amiable futilities as the number of angels dancing upon a needle point to fierce discussion of the constitution and attributes of the Godhead itself. The Byzantines were indefatigable in such dialectical exercises.

Ignorance, though not complete, was vast and widespread. All classical knowledge was at first contemned as pagan, and science and investigation of natural facts were, as Tertullian declared, unnecessary. Some ancient manuscripts were preserved in the monasteries, though many of these were used as material for writing devotional works, the old writing being scraped off. A certain proportion, however, survived all perils.

In the monasteries as in the outside world knowledge was scanty. It was necessary to decree in the seventh century that none should be raised to priest's orders unless he could read at least the Psalms and the order of baptism. Large numbers of monks were completely illiterate. Alfred, who re-established learning in England after the Danish invasions in the ninth century, bitterly lamented its decay. In the two previous centuries English scholarship and learning had been distinguished by such great names as Augustine, Theodore, the Greek Archbishop of Canterbury, the Venerable Bede, Boniface and others. At Alfred's accession there were, as he himself said, "few who could understand their service books in English or translate even a letter from Latin into English. . . . So few were there of them that I cannot remember even a single one south of the Thames when I succeeded to the kingdom."—(R. W. Chambers.) With the exception of the educational efforts of Charlemagne and the lamp of Greek learning that was kept burning, albeit somewhat dimly, in southern Italy, the general level in Europe was much below this before A.D. 1000. "All through the Middle Ages there was a great mass of lower parish clergy who, in fact, knew little more than their parishioners."—(Coulton.)

Although in practice the monks as part of their rule of charity relieved the sick and thereby played the part of physician, they were in general forbidden to do so. St. Bernard, the founder of the Cistercian order in the eleventh century, not only forbade his monks to practise or become students of medicine but also forbade them when sick to have anything to do with physic. "To buy drugs, to consult physicians, to take medicines, befits not religion." They must not use earthly remedies at the risk of salvation. Many of the legends of the saints present the same idea of the incompatibility of religious virtue and the treatment of disease by any means but prayer. On the other hand the huge Carolingian monastery at St. Gall included both a well-arranged hospital and a medicinal herb garden. There was undoubtedly much simple practice of simple medicine; as in other departments of life the monastic ideals were too austere for mortals of ordinary calibre.

We have chosen to attempt a brief note on the medieval background rather than to present strings of names of tedious writers and lengthy specimens of the futilities of medieval recipe books. It is obvious that if this attempt be a fair representation nothing in the way of medical science as we understand it could exist. In fact it did not—in Europe.

To show that the picture is not overdrawn and that the magic and superstition of the Assyrians do not suffer by comparison let us take a few examples from the well known "Anglo-Saxon Leechdoms," and other Saxon MSS. of the twelfth century and earlier, English documents which, as Dr. Singer states, "provide us with the best account of medical practice in the Dark Ages."

Not only are they valuable for this reason, but they also provide the opportunity to narrow somewhat the scope of our reading. From this point onwards where native material throws adequate light on the progress of medicine and hygiene we shall draw upon it in preference to Continental material.

These Saxon MSS. are in the main, christianized versions of Latin originals imperfectly translated from Apuleius Barbarus (his *Herbarium* appeared in multitudinous forms throughout medieval times), Dioscorides (the compiler of a great materia medica of authority unchallenged from the first to the fifteenth century) and others, with an admixture of Teutonic magic brought from the Saxon home-land. Some of these MSS. are beautifully illuminated. One in the British Museum, which is dated about 1050, contains hundreds of fine drawings of plants and animals freely copied from an Italian source, probably a late classical version of the *Apuleius* which it presents in duly modified form. Its frontispiece shows Chiron (the fabled centaur who first gathered simples) with Plato and Æsculapius both in Saxon dress. The figure labelled Plato is really, in the classical original form which the scribe copied, Apollo but he could not bring himself to do honour to a pagan deity. Another MS., which probably belonged to the Abbey of Glastonbury, was written about 950. It is an unillumined book of recipes and was translated and edited by Dr. Oswald Cockayne from whose work the following quotations are taken. The magic is simple in kind and simply accepted:

> Against mental vacancy and against folly; put into ale, bishopwort, lupins, betony, the southern or Italian fennel, nepte, water agrimony, cockle, marche; then let the man drink.

> Against a warty eruption, one must take seven little wafers, such as a man offereth with, and write these names on each wafer, Maximianus, Malchus, Iohannes, Martinianus, Dionysius, Constantinus, Serafion; then again one must sing the charm [not quoted here] first into the left ear, then into the right ear, then above the man's poll, then let one who is a maiden go to him and hang it upon his neck, do so for three days, it will soon be well with him.

PLATE XXIX
The Worm in Saxon Medicine

The most constant feature in the drawings of Saxon pseudo-medica. MS. is the worm (*see* also Plate XXVIII) who, as the cause of disease, came "to slay and to slaughter".

Ever he is to be defeated by magic, i.e. special herbs over which charms have been recited. This, one of the most primitive of all folk notions, is seen in the two drawings from Harleian MSS. 5294, where warriors, assisted by magic potions prepared by physicians, have slain worms and a scorpion, from whose bodies oozes the evil poison. The bulbous-rooted plant shown is labelled "Arnote", but it is not the earth-nut of the modern pharmacopœia.

British Museum.

PLATE XXIX

data inuilice diftrut uenenu.

Ad pē̄ sū ferro l̄ sude q̄ se iuier pauntr. Herba Aronu cū acero ipoſtra pſotiſſime

Nomen herbe. Cyclaminos. Omoeos. Ceteron.
Alii. Arcion. Alii. Cassofillos. Alii. Chedomon. Zoro
aftes. Chachena. Alii. Sampaues. dicunt. Alii. Boſtanes.

PLATE XXX

PLATE XXX

An Anglo-Norman Physician at His Patient's Bedside

This, one of a series of similar drawings from an Anglo-Norman MS. of the thirteenth century (Bodleian MSS., Ashmole 399), shows a physician who has pronounced, from examination of the patient's urine, that no hope remains. Urine inspection was throughout the medieval period regarded as the most important and reliable method of diagnosis. As noted in page 109 it lasted into the seventeenth century and the urine flask and urine charts were principal weapons in the doctor's armoury. Note that the physician is a layman, not an ecclesiastic.

Bodleian Library, Oxford ; photograph by courtesy of Dr. Charles Singer.

For the better digestion of meat taken; take lupins, lay them under the altar, sing over them nine Masses, that shall avail for meat taken; lay it under the vessel into which thou hast in mind to milk.

If wens at the heart pain a man, let a maiden go to a spring, which runs directly eastward, and ladle up a cup full, moving the cup with the stream, and let her or him sing over it the Creed and Paternoster, and then pour it into another vessel, and then ladle up some more, and again sing the Creed and the Paternoster, and so manage so as to have three cups full; do so for nine days, soon it will be well with the man.

Against a woman's chatter take at night, fasting, a root of radish; that day the chatter cannot harm thee.

The reverse case is also simply provided for:

In case a woman suddenly turn dumb, take pennyroyal and rub to dust, wind it up in wool, lay under the woman, it will soon be well with her.

The elements of Teutonic magic in these "leechdoms" are of considerable interest as well as of illustrative value. In serious cases of one type the priest is called in to assist the leech:

If horse or beast be elf-shot take seed of dock and Scotch wax. Let a priest sing twelve Masses over them and add holy water and then put that upon the horse or on what cattle soever it may be. Have the worts [herbs] always with thee.

The Saxon, according to Dr. Singer, held two main doctrines of disease. One was the existence of malicious elves who "shot" the darts of pain and disease into man and beast (whence elf-shot in the quotation) and another was the worm theory, a form of which we have already seen in ancient Mesopotamia. The worm was a terrifying creature who appears repeatedly in the MSS. illuminations [Plates 27, 28 and 29]. It presents a really extraordinary example of the persistence of primitive folk ideas in magic and medicines. Elves, worms and demons all produce disease in different varieties according to their nature and are to be dealt with by charm, exorcism, or as again in ancient medicine, by disgusting remedies to nauseate and drive them forth. Some mixtures are truly hideous and include animal excreta. These are milder examples:

For pricking sensation in the eye. Break to pieces a hound's head and bind it on. It healeth well.

For sore ears. Mix a bull's gall with honey and drop it in. Soon it will be well with them.

healthily situated Langobard city of Salerno the first regular medical school in Europe. Standing alone for two or three centuries it achieved a fame which was, according to some writers, in excess of its real due. Certainly to have studied there between the ninth and twelfth centuries sufficed to make the reputation of any practitioner. Record exists of a Salernitan physician to the queen of Charles the Simple of France at the end of the ninth century. But it was in the eleventh and twelfth centuries that its fame as the *Civitas Hippocratica* (the Hippocratic city) spread over Europe as being an abode of learning and an asylum for the sick. Certainly it did set a higher standard medically than the rest of Europe but of real scholarship and advanced medical learning we find little evidence. Its outstanding characteristic was that it was a secular institution and, until rival schools were set up in the days of its eclipse at Montpellier, Paris, Bologna and Padua, the only one at which no clerical status was required for its students. Its pride was its open mindedness and its reliance on sick bed experience but as elsewhere the experience was not deeply founded and we see, as Sudhoff puts it, but "the modest beginnings of a general art of healing."

Still, judged by contemporary standards, its work was very good. There is little room for doubt that the examination of those aspiring to practise medicine, which was enacted in 1140 by Roger II of Sicily (in whose kingdom of Apulia Salerno was included), was to be undertaken by the officers of the Salerno school, so far at least as the mainland was concerned. This decree, the first of its kind in Europe, is of particular interest:

> Whosoever will henceforth practise medicine, let him present himself to our officials and judges to be examined by them; but if he presume of his own temerity, let him be imprisoned and all his goods be sold by auction. The object of this is to prevent the subjects of our kingdom incurring peril through the ignorance of physicians.

In the next century that great man, the Emperor Frederick II, Stupor Mundi—as his half-horrified contemporaries called him, for he was a sceptic, a modern in politics, a freethinker with something of modern scientific inquiry in his thought, and a spurner of ecclesiastical control in any form—this man decreed not only license from Salerno but curriculum of study:

THE THIRTEENTH CENTURY PHYSICIAN RECEIVING AND VISITING PATIENTS

Taken from the same MS. as that represented in Plate XXX, the upper of these two delightfully ingenuous drawings shows the doctor seated while four patients wait upon him, with head or other troubles, having paid their fees to the doctor's assistant, who is seen on the right with a purse in his hand. Below, the physician departs on horseback the while the patient's family hold up their hands in delighted amazement at his profound wisdom.

Bodleian Library, Oxford MS. Ashmole 399 ; *photograph by courtesy of Dr. Charles Singer.*

PLATE XXXI

Plate XXXII

t audi quefo & faue pucab; uied. hoc quod peco a ce diua in prefta. uolens her
bis quascunq; generac cua maiestas salutis causa cribuas cunctis geucabus.
et ut in uniuctas medicinam cuam hanc fumi ad me cum arce unuierahsi se
quid e his facro: habeat euentum bonum. cui q; eisdem dedeis. pspd gcis
tribuis. in re cuncta reubuat. Merico eisdem a uir accipure: sanos eosdem qos
puies. nunc deus postulo. ut hoc in cua maiestas fistic: qd e supplex rogo;

PLATE XXXII
PAGAN MAGIC PRACTISED IN THE THIRTEENTH CENTURY

Saxon and Norman medical treatment depended in the main upon herb remedies. Of themselves they were too simple to be effective, and had to be reinforced by charms which, though often mingled with masses, were essentially pagan in character. In this thirteenth century illumination the physician (a layman, for he is not tonsured) is blessing the herbs. The prayer which he is uttering is entirely pagan, as the following partial translation shows:

"Earth, divine goddess, Mother Nature, Guardian of gods, thou art called Great Mother of the gods; thou art Queen of gods. O goddess, whatsoever herbs thy power doth produce, give, I pray, with goodwill and grant them me as medicines. Howsoever I use them and to whomsoever I give them, may they have good success. I pray thee as a supliant that by thy majesty thou grant me this."

Harleian MSS. 1585, British Museum.

Considering the harm which may arise from the ignorance of physicians, we ordain that no one shall henceforth practise physic unless he be first publicly examined by the masters at Salerno, and present testimonials, to ourselves or our representative, and receive from us or him licence to practise.

Since the science of medicine can never be understood without some previous knowledge of logic, we decree that none shall study medicine unless he have studied logic for at least three years. Then let him learn medicine for five years, and also surgery, which is a part of medicine.

According to Dr. Withington (from whom the above translations are taken) it is to the masters of Salerno that the title "doctor" in the sense in which we use it, was first given by Gilles (Ægidius) of Corbeil about 1200.

About the end of the eleventh century appeared a pseudo-poetic work which did more than anything to spread the fame of Salerno. This, was the "Regimen Sanitatis" or "Schola Salernitana" which, written in verse form for easy copying by careless scribes, presents the body of popular medicine of that day. Whether it actually originated from Salerno or was one of the many medieval literary cheats, as Dr. Fielding Garrison thinks, is immaterial. Translated into many languages it spread over the whole Western world including the British Isles. By the middle of the nineteenth century no fewer than two hundred and forty editions of the poem had been printed, in addition to the many MS. copies, over one hundred of which survive in European libraries. Some of its bits of proverbial wisdom survive yet, as in the often quoted line from Longfellow:

Joy, Temperance and Repose, slam the door on the doctor's nose
(From the *Singgedichte of Friedrich von Logan*).

The Latin text (1491 edition) runs thus:

Si tibi deficiant medici, medici tibi fiant
Haec tria, mens laeta, requies, moderata diaeta.

Which may be translated:

If you would do without doctors make your doctors
these three:
A Happy Mind, Rest and Moderate Diet.

Very matter of fact, and on the whole, sensible the verses deal with the forms of food which "be good to eat," herbs and their

CHAPTER VIII

THE DRY BONES STIR AND LEARNING AWAKES: A.D. 1200–1450

WE NOW begin to pick up again the threads of Greek science and medicine and remarkable beyond the primary fact of their preservation, are the wide journeyings necessary to pick them up. Up to the present our interests have been concentrated in comparatively narrow lands of Europe in one of which, at least, some not inconsiderable flavour of Greek physic lasted through even the Dark Ages. Now we follow the wanderings of Hippocratic, Aristotelian and Galenic learning through the Near East to Arabia and Persia, and on to distant Bokhara in Turkistan. Connections may even be traced in India and China.

When the civilization of the West finally collapsed into sordid ruin some copies of Greek works and some teachers of them survived. The means of these survivals were three. The most obvious one was the Greek empire of Byzantium but, as we have already indicated, theology and dialectic prevented it being more than a sterile storehouse of classical learning until its doors were flung open, somewhat rudely, at the fall of Constantinople in 1453. Then its precious collection of MSS. flowed freely into a Europe awakened and eager to profit by them. The least obvious was a heretical Christian sect, the Nestorians. The third, and most widely influential in the period now under review, were those great lovers of learning, the Arabs of the Eastern and Western Khalifates of the ninth to twelfth centuries.

It is a matter for reflection that if there was one incident more important than others that was responsible for keeping Greek medicine alive from the fifth to the fifteenth centuries it was an acrimonious theological dissension in the fifth century. Nestorius was bishop of Constantinople in 431, when a General Council of the Church excommunicated him, and deprived him of his see for his denial of the doctrine of Theotokos (that the Virgin Mary was the "Mother of God"). His condemnation and subsequent violent death led to the establishment of a new

THE FIRST REVIVAL OF MEDICINE THROUGH THE INFLUENCE OF THE ARABS

The map shows the wide dominions of Islam in the middle of the twelfth century, and indicates thereby the strong influence of Moslem learning upon Europe. Arabic culture was then much more advanced than that of Christian Europe, and in medicine and science it held all that was known from the Classical Period. All the surviving medical works of Greece were translated into Arabic.

The picture above, which shows a consultation with an Arabian physician, occurs in a portion of an Arabic translation, dated 1222, of the great Materia Medica of the Greek Dioscorides.

Arabic painting from Dr. F. R. Martin, "Miniatures, Painters and Paintings of India, Persia and Turkey."

PLATE XXXIII

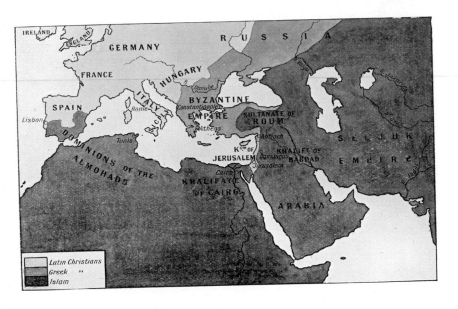

PLATE XXXIV

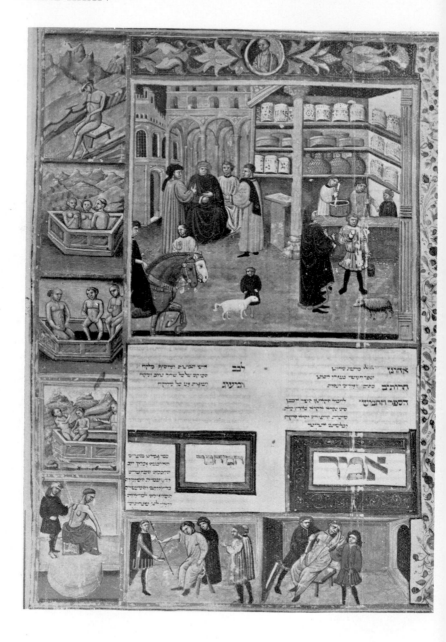

AVICENNA, "PRINCE OF PHYSICIANS", OF ARABIA, DEPICTED IN A JEWISH MS.

This leaf, from a fifteenth century Hebrew translation of the "Great Canon" of Avicenna (in the University Library, Bologna), is a somewhat late example of the great part played by Arab-speaking Jews in spreading the medical and scientific learning of Arabia through "Darkest Europe". In the principal miniature Avicenna,—or to give him his full sounding Arabic name,—Abu Ali Husayn Ibn-Abdullah Ibn Sina—in dark robes is seated, while his pupils dispute before him. The great importance of drug treatment in Arabic medicine is indicated by the well-stored drug shop on the right. The smaller miniatures represent various cases of disease and treatment by bathing, bleeding, etc.

Courtesy of Cavaliere Uff. Dr. Carlo Frati, Bologna.

communion, the Nestorian Church which, under a Catholicus, the Patriarch of the East, flourished for a thousand years in Persia, Mesopotamia, and Syria, and even established bishoprics so far afield as Central Asia, India and China. Relics of the sect even survived to come under British protection in Iraq during the Great War. The importance of the Nestorians in our study rests upon their preservation of Greek learning at their great centre Edessa, in Mesopotamia, where they established a successful school of medicine with two hospitals. Within sixty years the heretics were expelled from the empire by the orthodox emperor Zeno and their college buildings destroyed. Re-established across the frontier at Nisibis they were afterwards welcomed by Noshirwan (Chosroes I) under whom Persia attained the zenith of her power and culture in the sixth century. At the great university which he founded at Jundeshapur, Greek learning which the Nestorians had brought was eagerly studied, with the addition of Indian philosophy and medicine. Jundeshapur became the most famous school of Mahomedan medicine and the fountain head of Arabic medical lore from the eighth century onwards, whence some part of the stream of Greek learning was once more to flow back to Europe. Had the Nestorians not carried Greek medicine to Persia it is difficult to see how Europe (apart from the limited activities of South Italy discussed in the previous chapter) could have acquired any considerable bulk of Greek medicine before the fifteenth century, for Europe knew but little Greek until the teachers from Constantinople travelled abroad after the siege of 1453.

In the seventh century the victorious banner of Islam swept over the whole of the Near East and into Europe, and the heritage of classical culture passed into the hands of the Khalifs of the East and the West at Baghdad and at Cordova, who carefully fostered knowledge. As Dr. Stanley Lane-Poole says, "No more astonishing movement in the history of civilization has occurred than the sudden passion of the whole Islamic world for culture. . . . This was the supreme service of Islam to general culture." Baghdad with its great Hall of Science, built by the son of Haroun al-Raschid, Cordova with its school of renowned physicians, and Toledo the centre from which, after its capture by Christian forces in 1085, a stream of translations issued—all were bright glowing stars in the firmament of Arab learning. "Islam led the vanguard of progress and the Muslims taught the world," says the emir Ali. For the

H

knew and practised but negligible portions of Hippocrates and Galen's permanently valuable work. The Scholastic mind was more concerned with arrangement, argument and annotation than with the ideas presented. Direct observation is rarely attempted or considered; the authority of a master—Aristotle or Galen—is sufficient to settle any difficulty though the master be quoted inaccurately from a hopelessly corrupt text or his words be twisted by dialectic ingenuity out of all semblance to real meaning.

There yet remains the fact that these translations and commentaries, corrupt and nearly dead though they were, were primarily responsible for the first revival of learning. It was the late twelfth and thirteenth centuries that saw the beginnings of the universities, "these new thinking shops," as Dr. Coulton calls them, and it was on these Arabic-Latin text books that their students were mainly fed and continued to be so fed long after the Renaissance. Oxford and Cambridge began in the mid-thirteenth century but the great medical centres were at the universities of Montpellier (which, said to be founded in the early twelfth century definitely superseded Salerno in the thirteenth), Bologna, Paris and Padua. The teaching was mainly by word of mouth, for it was a bookless age. At the end of the fourteenth century the library of the Paris medical school consisted of no more than twelve books (MSS.), mostly Arabian, of which the immense *Continens* of Rhazes was the most important—a significant light on the scope of medical education, since Paris was a school of real importance. This is perhaps partly explained by the fact that medicine ranked low in the list of university faculties. The greater figures in medicine studied, not at one university, as would suffice for a modern student, but at all. Learning and practice were both personal to the teacher.

This flowering of the university system was in itself a very significant change. In the earlier centuries learning hardly existed outside the Church. It was a foregone conclusion that a literate man would be in orders of some kind. Now knowledge was opening its bounds and so long as it avoided heresy, a matter of some difficulty, it was free. At most of the universities, including Oxford, medical degrees of bachelor, licentiate and doctor were given; Continental medical education was of course earlier than English. At the beginning of the fourteenth century Bologna was foremost. There Mundinus, a professor, revived the study of anatomy which had been almostly com-

PLATE XXXV

GATHERING SIMPLES AND COMPOUNDING DRUGS FROM A MS.
OF A MASTER OF SALERNO

In Salerno, the twelfth-century centre of medical learning, two writers, whose names stand out in advance of the spread of Arabian learning, were Roger of Salerno and Roland of Parma. The writings of both are mainly of surgical interest, but in the charming set of drawings from a thirteenth century French MS. of Roger we see many illustrations of purely medical practice.

In the two upper drawings the physician is supervising the operations of assistants who bring him herbs for identification, pound them in mortars and brew them over a fire. In the lower drawing a doctor has tied a bandage, with a most unprofessional knot, round the patient's nose.

Trinity College, Cambridge, MS. O.1.20.

PLATE XXXV
Gathering Simples and Compounding Drugs from a MS. of a Master of Salerno

In Salerno, the twelfth-century centre of medical learning, two writers, whose names stand out in advance of the spread of Arabian learning, were Roger of Salerno and Roland of Parma. The writings of both are mainly of surgical interest, but in the charming set of drawings from a thirteenth century French MS. of Roger we see many illustrations of purely medical practice.

In the two upper drawings the physician is supervising the operations of assistants who bring him herbs for identification, pound them in mortars and brew them over a fire. In the lower drawing a doctor has tied a bandage, with a most unprofessional knot, round the patient's nose.

Trinity College, Cambridge, MS. O.1.20.

PLATE XXXV

mester seria sil metez od une penne dele es chief des

He aposteme uent entre les narilles.rilles.
q̃ e polipus apele le greignur auent entre les nar

ble bein. ſ puis metez en ſaſ. poz dolur des ozailles.

PLATE XXXVI

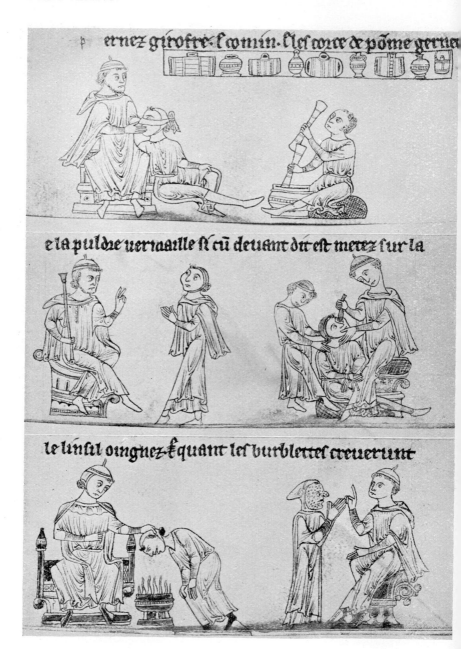

PLATE XXXVI
Patients of a Thirteenth Century Doctor

These further drawings, from the Cambridge MS. of Roger of Salerno, depict (top) salve being applied to an injured eye: the arrival and subsequent treatment of a patient with an exaggerated abscess due to infection from a decayed tooth: one patient being subjected to a somewhat drastic form of heat treatment for a skin disease: while another presents himself with a severe rash—probably intended to represent leprosy.

Trinity College, Cambridge, MS. O.1.20.

pletely neglected since Galen. Among his students was the cultured Guy de Chauliac, "the restorer of surgery" who displayed a righteous scorn for his contemporaries for they "despise everything not sanctioned by custom and authority forgetting that, as Aristotle declares, these are the two great hindrances to the discovery of the truth."

Earlier than Bologna was Montpellier which, being placed in south-eastern France, within reach of Spain, was more accessible to Hispano-Moorish influence and had accordingly the advantage over Paris and other medical schools in its great store of MSS. of Arabian origin. Medicine was taught there in the twelfth century although the Papal Bull founding the university only dates from 1289. Among its great teachers were Arnald of Villanova, Henry of Mondeville and Guy de Chauliac, the last two being surgeons. Arnald (died in 1312) was a prolific Scholastic writer of the Arabian and Salernitan tradition and was one of the earliest editors of the *Regimen Sanitatis* of Salerno discussed in the previous chapter. Sudhoff credits him with its authorship. Theologian, lawyer, philosopher, alchemist and physician, friend of a Pope and a convicted heretic, he was undoubtedly a man of parts. His balance is indicated by his dictum that "the modest and wise physician will never hasten to drugs unless compelled by necessity." Nevertheless he spent much effort in the search for a universal remedy, an elixir which should restore youth to the old. Some of the virtues of such a potion he found in the *aqua vitæ* or alcohol (an Arabian original word) which also had the valuable property of extracting the essence of herbs and roots whence come the "extracts" and "tinctures" of the pharmacist.

Many other names might be quoted. Padua (Shakespere's "fair nursery of Arts") had Peter of Abano, a scholiast who tried conclusions with the Inquisition and escaped the stake by dying in his bed; Peter of Lisbon, who became Pope John XXI; and others.

It is not difficult to prepare a catalogue with summaries and extracts of medieval physicians and writers on medicine whose works have survived and to present such a catalogue—perhaps selected to support a brief,—as a picture of later medieval medicine. Although this method might produce interesting and even amusing results without departing from fact it would not be a true picture because it would be neither complete nor would it indicate clearly any line of advance, any progress in the stream of thought, that might exist. We have indicated the importance of studying nature rather than books, produced the first scientific botany since Dioscorides (the fourth century Greek) in which he uses the phrase "All that is set down here is the result of our own experience . . . experience can only be of certainty." Medical works were among his writings which were widely read. His contemporaries suspected him of magic —they called him "Great in magic"—because of his wide learning.

It may not unreasonably be said that with men of this calibre interested in medicine there was hope for its general advancement. That advance, in spite of the enormous stir of the Renaissance which we shall comment on in our next chapter, was unfortunately slow in coming, and when we consider the mass of popular medicine in these centuries the reason is fairly clear. We may give an example of this material. In 1276 Peter of Lisbon, who had studied at the medical schools of Paris and Montpellier, became both physician to Pope Gregory X and Cardinal Bishop of Tusculum. The same year, as Pope John XXI, he succeeded Gregory. Having sufficient learning and intelligence to rise to the supreme headship of the Church he is nevertheless the author of an extremely popular book of prescriptions taken from writers of every kind and selected with so complete a lack of discrimination as to include the following from a contemporary writer, called Gilbert the Englishman:

> Gilbert's ointment for gout: Take a very fat puppy and skin him, then take juice of wild cucumber, rue, pellitory, ivy berries, juniper berries, euphorbium, castoreum, fat of vulture, goose, fox and bear, equal parts, and stuff the puppy therewith. Then boil him: add wax to the grease that floats on the surface and make an ointment. Or, if you like, take a frog when neither sun nor moon is shining; cut off its hind legs and wrap them in deer skin; apply the right to the right and the left to the left foot of the gouty person, and without doubt he will be healed.

The reader is asked to turn back to page 34 and contrast the formula with the Egyptian use of weird animal fats for stiffness and ask himself what progress is represented here in an interval of two thousand seven hundred years. Even the Assyrian pharmacopœia fails to produce a remedy quite so futile. Dr. Jastrow discussing Babylonian and Assyrian medicine comments shrewdly on this type of therapeutic:

PLATE XXXVII
Miniatures from the Vienna MS. of the "Tacuinum Sanitatis"

The three known MSS. of the work of the Arabian physician, Albucasis of Cordova (translated about 1276 by order of Charles of Anjou), are practically identical with but slight variations in the miniatures which adorn them. One from the Venice MS. is given in colour as a frontispiece to this volume.

Two other examples from the Vienna MS. are given here. On the left camphor is being sold, and on the right theriac, the most famous of all medieval drug preparations, the universal antidote. Said to have been invented by Mithridates, king of Pontus, theriac was an electuary with a massive formula (the "Dispensatory" of Cordus, 1546, gave it sixty-four ingredients) which appeared in various forms in all formularies and pharmacopœias from Roman times down to the German Pharmacopœia of 1882.

Courtesy of Prof. Dr. J. Bick, Director-General of the National Library, Vienna.

PLATE XXXVII

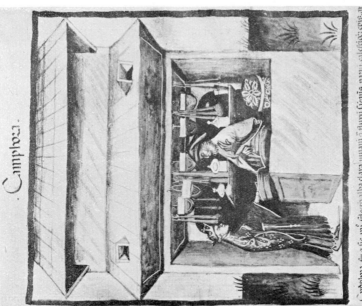

Camphora.

Camphora. fri.i.ſic.mi. ſicco alba clara. quam̄ ō ſiccui ſiguiſ narni. caleſtaſ. epſ. ar aceerunleσ. n felicſı agitaσ. Maxime. pſtar i ſiccedo unguie. z aer uaσ o orru. Rem̄ non eꝉ molei z nemture. Quiσ gnat reteceraõ. Quenic mag. ſiquuanıſ. elıare in z̄ aalıbʒ.

Tructa.

Tructa. x pto ca. ſic. Sicco que tleir gallum. auenσ ꝯq̄ panſir. x. anni. quinī ōſuenaſ z gentule. ca. xtro uaum. p. v. anne. ſuer uiglue. Rem̄o nerı. oı friguerurıb̄. ıtra ōuo noenir mag. ſrı ſoiuſ hvenιe z ıegıolισ. frıe uͨ abuσ ırı. eo ſuır uſuır.

PLATE XXXVIII

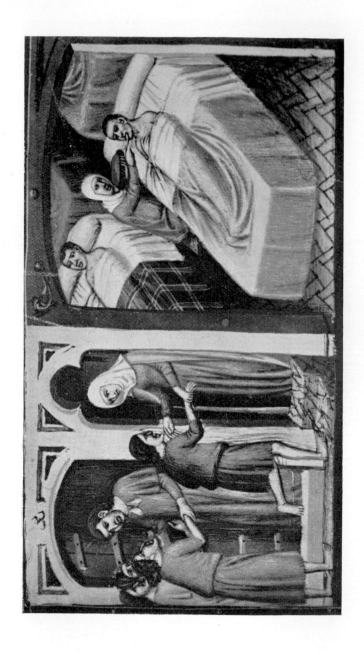

PLATE XXXVIII
Thirteenth Century Infirmary for the Sick

Although it is often said that hospitals existed throughout medieval times there were no hospitals in the modern sense of the term in Europe. The many hospitals and almhouses which did exist catered, primarily, for the inmates' spiritual needs, the physical care of the sick consisting mainly of the provision of beds and food and simple, though kindly, attention. These scenes, from a French MS. of about 1250, illustrate the reception and care of the afflicted. Note that, as was a medieval custom, the patients lie naked in their beds.

Bibliothèque Nationale Paris, MS. lat. 8846: photo, Catala.

In the popular remedies of Middle Ages which mark the return of methods the very reverse of scientific and which survive as extra-medicinal elements of our own civilisation, relegated to root and herb doctors and to quacks of all kinds, we may see the continual influence of those ideas and practices which prevented Babylonian-Assyrian medicine from rising superior to its surroundings.

This Gilbert was, says Dr. Singer, the first English physician to make a reputation on the Continent. He studied at Salerno in the early thirteenth century, and produced a voluminous *Compendium of Medicine*, about 1240, based partly on the *Chirurgia* of Roger of Salerno (beautiful MSS. of which exist in the British Museum and at Trinity College, Cambridge—see Plates 35, 36), and for medical matters on the usual Arab authorities. He is one of the two English physicians mentioned by Chaucer in the list of medical authorities in the Prologue to the "Canterbury Tales" where the "doctour of phisyk" is described. The other was John of Gaddesden who took the degree of doctor of medicine at Oxford about 1309, and wrote a lively and popular work, *Rosa Anglica*, about 1314. Medically it was in no way superior to Gilbert's compilation. Guy de Chauliac says of it "I thought to find in it an odour of suavity and I found the fables of Pope John, Gilbert and Theodoric."

Of the state of medicine in England we may judge clearly by the statutes of the university of Oxford about 1325 as quoted by Dr. Gunther in his *Early Science in Oxford*:

> Those skilled in medicine are reckoned more learned than others, since to their discretion are committed the cure of the sick, the perils of death and the ordering of life. Great care must therefore be exercised that only competent persons are allowed to practise or incept in that faculty.

For inception in medicine, we read, the candidate must have read one book of Galen and one of Hippocrates (the *Aphorisms*) for theory and others for practice. For license, book learning for six years was required. No mention is made of clinical experience or of anatomical knowledge. The earliest recorded lecturer on medicine was Nicolas Tingewick, of Balliol, who says Dr. Gunther, was gratefully remembered by Edward I as the physician "to whom after God, we owe thanks for our recovery from the illness which lately oppressed us." (October, 1306.) This recovery was an extremely expensive form of faith-healing for the apothecary's bill for the drugs used amounted

CHAPTER IX

FOUNDATION OF THE MODERN PERIOD OF MEDICINE:
1450–1600

In 1451 Mohammed II, lord of the Ottoman Empire, and terror of Christendom prepared for the grand attack on Constantinople. For over a century the city with its long walls had preserved its existence by alternating tribute with defiance to the Turkish power. Hitherto, the fortress state on the Bosporus had been impregnable, but when the great siege began in earnest in 1453 only a few months passed before the final assault by sea and by land was launched and on May 29th the last of the Greek emperors disappeared in the slaughter and sack. With him vanished the last centre where the regular language of Court and Church was that of the philosophers and dramatists of fifth century Athens and of Hippocrates himself. The libraries, still stored with the MSS. of ancient Greek learning, were destroyed and their contents and their custodians dispersed abroad. Mostly they fled to Italy.

This catastrophic event but accelerated the change which was developing in intellectual Europe. There had been signs, amid the stagnation of dying medievalism, of the coming flood tide of humanism. Nearly sixty years earlier Chrysoloras, a man of scholarship, had been appointed to the chair of Greek at Florence and Nicholas V, who was elected Pope in 1437 mainly on account of his scholarship, had earlier distinguished himself by discovering the medical portion, *De Medicina*, of a general encyclopædia written by a Roman gentleman, Cornelius Celsus, in the age of Cicero. Since this work contained an excellent historical account of Greek medicine it was of great value and absorbing interest to medical men of the fifteenth century who had never before had access to an uncorrupted classical work.

With the election of the enthusiastic humanist Æneas Sylvius as Pope Pius II in 1458 we may see the semi-official overthrow of Scholasticism. Everywhere the clerks are busy copying the new marvels. For the first time the actual words of the classical masters can be read, untouched by theology and unspoiled by translation

PLATE XXXIX

THE FIFTEENTH CENTURY DOCTOR HOLDS HIS DAILY "SURGERY"

The physician is distinguished by his fur lappets. As is common in many medieval drawings the artist wishing to show two separate actions has drawn the doctor twice. In the first case, he is attending to the injured arm of a young man: in the second, he is gravely examining the patient's urine in the inevitable flask. Outside other sadly injured patients limp to his door.

British Museum, Royal MS. 15 E.2.

PLATE XXXIX

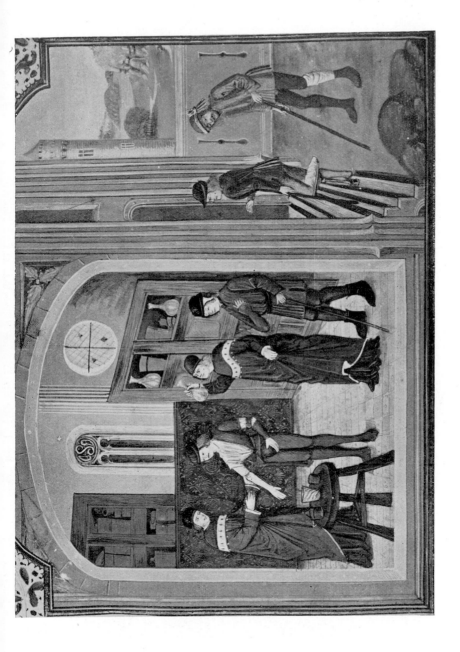

PLATE XL

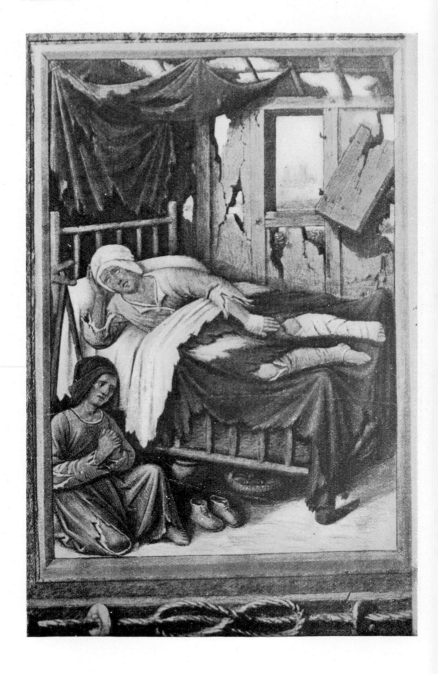

PLATE XL

SQUALOR OF A PEASANT'S HOVEL ABOUT THE YEAR 1500

Late as it is, this French painting well illustrates the conditions of life for the peasant throughout the greater part of the Middle Ages. The sanitationless squalor of their thatched hovels of wattle and daub, with unglazed windows and earth floors, was in utter contrast with the fairly hygienic condition of the Ancient World. Health and hygiene were, of course, absent and the expectation of life from the twelfth to the sixteenth centuries was so low that a man of fifty was regarded as an old man. In France these conditions lasted in many places up to the time of the Revolution. In England the persistence of plague among the peasants compelled the attention of the authorities to the utter lack of rural hygiene and the first Sanitary Act was passed in 1388: little real improvement was achieved before Tudor days.

From Bouchot, " L'exposition des primitifs francais," permission of Librairie centrale des Beaux Arts.

PLATE XL

SQUALOR OF A PEASANT'S HOVEL ABOUT THE YEAR 1500

Late as it is, this French painting well illustrates the conditions of life for the peasant throughout the greater part of the Middle Ages. The sanitationless squalor of their thatched hovels of wattle and daub, with unglazed windows and earth floors, was in utter contrast with the fairly hygienic condition of the Ancient World. Health and hygiene were, of course, absent and the expectation of life from the twelfth to the sixteenth centuries was so low that a man of fifty was regarded as an old man. In France these conditions lasted in many places up to the time of the Revolution. In England the persistence of plague among the peasants compelled the attention of the authorities to the utter lack of rural hygiene and the first Sanitary Act was passed in 1388: little real improvement was achieved before Tudor days.

From Bouchot, "L'exposition des primitifs français," permission of Librairie centrale des Beaux Arts.

and—equally fortunate—there are men of Greek tongue, ready and able to teach and interpret. The learned world appreciates to the full the treasures that have fallen to it and the scholars and students of Europe flock to Italy. For the next century they work hard at editing and translating helped immensely, in their task of spreading the light of the classical world and humanizing the medieval world, by the new invention of printing.

It is not, perhaps, surprising that the advance in scholarship was not equalled by the advance in medicine. The notions of experimental science were in existence but the tradition of the schools was too strong to permit any immediate application of the new knowledge. Even printing did not help greatly. Sir William Osler notes in a bibliographical monograph that of one hundred and eighty-two editions of medical books printed before 1480 only six were classical: including Pliny's *Natural History* (1469), Hippocrates (1473), Galen (1475), and Celsus *De Medicina* (1478). Inevitably some clung to the masters they knew—the Arabs. Montpellier University at their head persisted, as we have noted, into the seventeenth century.

Inevitably also persisted the dead hand of medievalism. While the schools of Italy hummed with the disputations of the new scholarship Montpellier and Oxford slept and Avicenna ruled. Some features lasted well beyond the recognized limit of the Middle Ages. Dr. Gunther notes that right into the middle of the sixteenth century figures of the Zodiac man in which every part of the body was assigned its Zodiacal figure were still being printed. *A Prognostication*, by Leonard Digges, "imprynted within the blacke Fryars", 1555, gives "a conducible note for letting bludde":

> These signes are mooste daungerous for bludde letting, the *Moone* beyinge in them, *Taurus*, *Gemini*, *Leo*, *Virgo*, and *Capricorne* with the laste half of *Libra* and *Scorpius*.

The practice of astrology and horoscopy required that the medical man should possess skill in mathematics, a connection which undoubtedly played its part in the formation of the iatro-mathematical school of medicine which flourished in the seventeenth century, and is commented on in its place.

Another medieval factor which persisted in exaggerated form even into the seventeenth century, was diagnosis by inspection of the patient's urine—uroscopy. For some four centuries it was so general a method that the flask used, the urinal, became the physicians' sign and urine conditions were systematized in

A blacke plastre devised by the Kinges hieghnes
Take
    gummi armoniaci oz. iiij,
    olei omphacini [olive oil] oz. ii,
    fyne thebinthine oz. vj,
    gummi Elemi [i.e. of a special cedar], j,
    Resun pini oz. x.
Boyle them together strongly on a soft fyre of coolys in a faire basyn, allwayes styrring it untill it be plaster-wyse; and so make it uppe in rolles, and kepe it to your vse.

Henry VIII was much concerned with the medical profession. In addition to the first Act already mentioned and the more famous one of 1540 incorporating the Barber-Surgeons' Company as depicted by Holbein, he secured the passage of four other Acts dealing with surgeons and medicine. Before his regulating Acts the actual daily practice of medicine was in the hands of the barbers and apothecaries. The physicians were few and mainly in the service of the nobles and the crown. Companies of these "barbers" existed in the principal towns from the fifteenth century. A grant of Arms to the London company in 1451 speaks of them as "Masters of Barbery and Surgery within the Craft of Barbery." The apothecaries were recognized in the last of Henry's medical statutes which empowered unlicensed folk to treat simple diseases. The Act mentions these "persons not being surgeons" with praise for their charitable dealings with the poor. The Apothecaries' Company belongs to a later century.

So the world is once more in possession of the true wisdom —not the teleologically twisted tradition—of the ancients, and if it and even the primary work of the great men of the two following centuries, of Vesalius and Harvey, did not materially alter the current medical practice, its indirect influence was sufficient to arouse that spirit of enquiry which brought modern medical science into being. Among those who worked in this spirit and so assisted not only in the spread of true humanism and the eventual triumph of science in medicine a few outstanding names may be mentioned. Francois Rabelais, the humorist and satirist, did much to promote scientific teaching of anatomy and of botany. His studies in the latter subject along with the work of Leonhard Fuchs and Otto von Brunfels, whose splendid herbals were illustrated with drawings of exquisite art taken from the living plants, did much to improve

PLATE XLI

German Physician of the Type Against which Paracelsus Fulminated

These illustrations from coloured woodcuts which date from 1491, two years before the birth of Paracelsus, give adequate representations of the average type of the German doctor of the late fifteenth and early sixteenth centuries. On the left, a woodcut, illustrating a chapter headed "De Urinis," clearly exemplifies the immensely exaggerated importance attached to uroscopy. Physicians and assistants declaim and demonstrate the conditions represented by no fewer than twenty urine bottles. Comic relief is supplied at the foot.

The second woodcut shows doctor and learned professor, in university gown, engaged in earnest disputation, while patients in every variety of condition and disorder are, so to speak, strewn around.

These woodcuts are taken from an immensely popular German Herbal which, originally printed at Mainz in 1485 as the *Herbarius zu Teutsch*, became in 1491 the better known *Hortus Sanitatis*, of which a very large number of editions were printed.

British Museum.

PLATE XLI

PLATE XLII

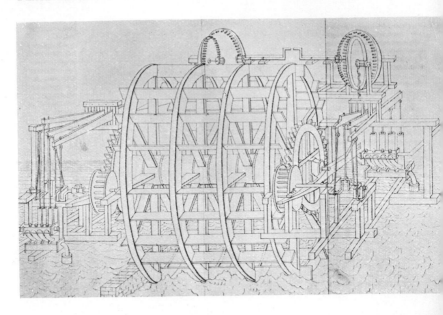

PLATE XLII
OLD LONDON BRIDGE AND ITS WATER-WORKS

A successful tidal pump for supplying river water to London was installed in one of the arches of old London Bridge by Peter Morrys in 1582. The excerpt from Visscher's View of London, 1610, shows the bridge from the Southwark side, the water-works being established under the arches at the city end.

The engineer's drawing of one of these tidal wheel pumps, from 'Hydraulia' by W. Matthews, 1835, based upon a description by Beighton in the *Philosophical Transactions*, 1731, shows the double set of pumps worked by gearing and cranked levers (somewhat in the manner of Trevithick's famous steam pumping-engine), connected on either side of the four-rimmed water-wheel. This system lasted until 1822, and had its own effects in increasing the obstruction of the river at the already obstructive bridge. An example of the other type of source of supply, the conduit head, is seen in Plate LV.

the accurate preparation and administration of drugs. Joannes Montanus, teacher of John Caius of Cambridge, developed scientific methods in disease investigation. Francis Bacon was in some respects in advance of his age. His method of inductive and experimental science laid down in the *Novum Organum* pointed out the right road to sound knowledge but had little or no effect on the medical science of the two centuries in which he lived. He has been given the credit of being the first thinker to understand the scientific importance of the Hippocratic system of clinical record; it is discussed in *The Dignity and Advancement of Learning*. William Gilbert, President of the Royal College of Physicians and court physician to Elizabeth and James I is noteworthy for his work on magnetism, *De Magnete*, which founded the science of electricity. His researches are mentioned in the *Novum Organum* as examples of the true method of experiment and deduction.

The Elizabethan period was, as even the schoolboy knows, one of great activity of spirit and military adventure. Surgeons were attached to the Crown forces, and several of them have left works of importance and interest. On the medical side are one or two printed books, such as *Bullein's Bulwarke of Defence against all Sicknes, Sorres, and Woundes, that dooe daily assaulte mankinde*, published in 1579, after his death, an original composition. He also wrote *A Comfortable Regiment against Pleurisi* (1562).

A writer of unusual interest, at least to the present study, was Andrew Borde, '*Doctor of Phisicke*,' and author of

> The Breviarie of Health: Wherein doth follow, remedies, for all manner of sicknesses and diseases, the which may be in Man or Woman. Expressing the obscure termes of Greke, Araby, Latin, Barbary, and English, concerning Phisicke and Chirurgerie.

This work, first published in 1547, and several times reprinted, contains curious yet clear lights on the hygiene of the sixteenth century. Sir Clifford Allbutt says that Borde not only "visited and revisited the universities of the continent," but was, "perhaps, the first writer on sanitation after the passing of Salerno and perhaps the first after Hippocrates to discuss the aspect and health of the dwelling house." We give two extracts from the 1575 edition of the *Breviarie* :

Of the Pestilence.

Epidimea is the greke word. In latin it is named Pestilencia, or Febris pestilencialis. In Englishe it is named the pestilence.

I

shows the first small beginnings of tropical medicine. Dr. Charles Singer has reproduced in facsimile one of the earliest works designed to meet this need. It is entitled *The Cures of the Diseased, in Remote Regions. Preventing Mortalitie, incident in Forraine Attempts of the English Nation* (London, 1598). Dr. Singer has established the authorship as belonging to George Wateson or Whetstone, an Elizabethan poet and gallant, who fought in the Low Countries and went with Humphrey Gilbert to Newfoundland. It is little more than a pamphlet, as its contents (in rhyme) show:

The Bookes Content

The burning Feuer, calde the CALENTURE,
The aking TABARDILLA pestilent,
Th' ESPINLAS prickings, which men do endure,
CAMERAS DE SANGRE, Fluxes violent,
Th' ERIZIPILA, swelling the Pacient,
The TINOSO, which we the SCURUEY call,
Are truly here describ'd, and cured all.

Calenture is sunstroke, Tabardilla, yellow fever or a form of plague, Espinlas, prickly heat, Cameras de Sangre, the bloody flux or dysentery, Erizipila, erysipelas, Tinoso, scurvy. Whetstone comments on the use by "the Indians and many other savage people" of the juice of "Tobacco" in poisoning and other conditions. We may briefly remark that this was one of many new drugs which came to Europe after the discovery of America. Most of them were described and figured in John Frampton's *Joyfull Newes out of the Newe Founde Worlde* of 1577. "Tabaco," as he calls it, was then considered as a specific against the new disease syphilis. Other new drugs were hiuourake (guaicum), ipecacuanha, and later, cinchona, or Peruvian bark, said to have been used to cure a Jesuit in Peru about 1600 (its tercentenary in 1930 dated from the first definite European knowledge of the drug). Its importance in the treatment of malaria cannot, of course, be over-estimated.

We have discussed the scientists, the scholars and the practical men. There remain the mystics and reformers who are summed up in a remarkable and difficult figure of intriguing and perpetual interest—the man who, born Von Hohenheim, called himself, or was called, Theophilus Aureolus Bombastes Furioso von Hohenheim, and, shortly, Paracelsus. His name added a word to the language—"bombastic"—which his enemies in his lifetime and his many detractors since have used against him with destroying scorn. He was a German and German scholarship lead by Sudhoff has done much to rehabilitate him. To men of his age he was offensive to the last degree for, as in every revolution there are those who wish to destroy the whole of the existing system, so the revolt from the schools called the Renaissance produced in Paracelsus its chief iconoclast. He was born in Switzerland in 1493, son of a physician. He wandered throughout Europe until he was 30, taking his degree as doctor of medicine at Ferrara in 1515. Between that time and 1536 he planned and, in part executed, a number of comprehensive medical works as well as an immense number of individual studies distinguished by impetuous originality, a wealth of observation and ever increasing knowledge.

As a reformer who cared not to mince his words Paracelsus quickly stirred up enmity on his appointment as city physician of Basle and lecturer in medicine at the university. He committed the unforgivable offences of lecturing in the common tongue instead of the professional Latin (he was the first to do so) and of denouncing the elaborate prescriptions, containing sixty or more items, of the day. He told his colleagues roundly.

> This is the cause of the misery in this world—that your science is founded upon lies. You are not professors of the truth, but professors of falsehood. It is not the opinions which a person holds, but the work which he performs, that constitutes a physician.
> This doctorship—this true understanding—is not conferred by emperors or popes, or high schools, but is a gift of God. I am protecting my kingdom, not with empty talk, but with the power of the arcana (mysteries); not with such as are bought in apothecary shops, but with the arcana of Nature, such as have been revealed to me by Nature herself.

He followed this with the more spectacular crime of beginning his course of university lectures with a public burning of the works of Galen and Avicenna. In the introduction to his *Paramirum* he says:

> You are to be my followers, and not I yours. Me! Me! I say, you will follow—You, Avicenna, Galen, Rhazes, Montagnana, and Mesues. I shall not be your follower, but you shall be mine. You men of Montpellier, and Cologne, and Vienna, you Germans, men of the Danube and Rhine, and the Maritime Islands, Athenians, Greeks, Arabs, and Israelites—I am not to follow you, but you shall follow me; nor will anyone hide even in the darkest corner. I am to be the monarch, and the monarchy will belong to me. . . .

Valentine was an independent person (the curious *Triumphal Chariot of Antimony* appeared at the end of the sixteenth century under his name) Paracelsus was a plagiarist.

His other concrete merits may be stated in a few words and, despite characteristics unsympathetic to the modern mind, he must have had merits or he would not have been the friend of so scholarly and critical a humanist as Erasmus. Certainly he condemned polypharmacy—"the longer the prescription the less the virtue"—and he also poured scorn on the infantile practice of uroscopy which, as we have seen, survived so late in time. He insisted on moderation in bleeding and on keeping wounds clean. A signal merit in the eyes of admirers of the Hippocratic ideal is the high respect which he avowed for the teachings of Hippocrates while rejecting practice founded on Galen, Rhazes and Avicenna.

There we leave him and his times. Before we continue the consideration of the development in the next century of the ideas and forces which his volcanic energy in part set free, we must turn back to discuss, very briefly, a factor of the greatest medical importance throughout the centuries of the Christian era—the story of infection and epidemic, of plague and pestilence.

PLATE XLIII

AROMATICS TO KEEP OFF PLAGUE

Ideas more or less vague concerning infection were forced upon those who lived in the plague centuries. A very general notion was that since the air was polluted infection could be warded off by sweetening it, as by the burning or other use of aromatic substances. The idea persisted until the nineteenth century in the judges' bunches of sweet-smelling herbs supposed, though repeatedly found to be ineffective, to preserve them from gaol fever (typhus). One form regularly adopted in plague epidemics was the pomum ambræ, an "amber apple," made up with aromatic drugs and amber or resin. It was to be smelt continuously as in this drawing of 1493 of a physician feeling the pulse of a plague patient, which illustrated a Venetian work on the plague by Piero Tassignano.

From *Charles Singer*, 'Fasciculi di Medicina' in "*Monumenta Medica*."

PLATE XLIII
AROMATICS TO KEEP OFF PLAGUE

Ideas more or less vague concerning infection were forced upon those who lived in the plague centuries. A very general notion was that since the air was polluted infection could be warded off by sweetening it, as by the burning or other use of aromatic substances. The idea persisted until the nineteenth century in the judges' bunches of sweet-smelling herbs supposed, though repeatedly found to be ineffective, to preserve them from gaol fever (typhus). One form regularly adopted in plague epidemics was the pomum ambre, an "amber apple," made up with aromatic drugs and amber or resin. It was to be smelt continuously as in this drawing of 1493 of a physician feeling the pulse of a plague patient, which illustrated a Venetian work on the plague by Piero Tassignano.

From Charles Singer, 'Fascicule di Medicina' in " Monumenta Medica."

PLATE XLIII

PLATE XLIV

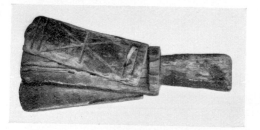

PLATE XLIV
MEDIEVAL ENEMIES, LEPROSY AND PLAGUE

The leper's distinguishing clothing and his warning clapper, two of the means by which he was compulsorily cut off from intercourse with his fellows and the spread of the disease checked, are well seen in this illumination from the fifteenth century *Miroir Historial* of Vincent de Beauvais. An example of an English leper's wooden clapper from the Wellcome Museum is also shown.

Bibliothèque de l'Arsenal, Paris, MS. 5080; *photo, Giraudon.*

The frightful mortality which resulted from the Black Death is indicated by this host of coffin bearers and sextons at Tournai in the Low Countries, in 1349. The illumination is taken from the *Annales* of Gilles (Aegidius) Le Muisis, who was abbot of St. Martin at Doornik.

Bibliothèque Royale, Brussels, MS. 13076; *photo, Giraudon.*

CHAPTER X

THE ENEMIES OF MAN: PLAGUE AND EPIDEMIC

IN THE foregoing chapters reference to specific diseases has been omitted except in so far as it was necessary to give examples showing the antiquity of disease and ancient methods of dealing with it. Broadly, medicine is best considered, especially in early times, as dealing with general conditions rather than with specific ailments. The persistence of the sterile doctrine of the humours—whose derangement was, for fifteen or more centuries, thought to be the root cause of disease—is sufficient to justify this attitude. The vast mass of medieval drug pharmacy and recipe treatment had little more than a pragmatic, rule-of-thumb relation to the diseases they pretended or seemed to cure. It is remarkable in fact how little of value has survived. Accordingly we have preferred to discuss health and ill-health and medical and hygienic methods rather than to fill our pages with antiquarian descriptions of ill-diagnosed and misunderstood diseases which can only interest the technical historian of medicine.

Here, however, we pause in our general survey and look back to consider a theme of despair which arises periodically from the earlier to the later times: the helplessness of man in the face of his cruellest enemy—"the pestilence that walketh in darkness . . . the destruction that wasteth at noonday" (Ps. xci. 6). The cry of the Hebrew smitten by the pestilence sent by the Lord in His wrath, the Saxon shuddering at the "vile flying things" or "venoms" which he considered to be the cause of epidemic disease, the utter terror and horror of men of the fourteenth century and the hideous devastations of Elizabethan and Jacobean England, where "death hath pitcht his tents"—all reflect the common factor of complete helplessness in the onset and awful progress of plague. Physician, priest, king and government, alderman and official—none could check its sway and most sought refuge in flight, thereby only spreading it further abroad.

This helplessness was due to lack of knowledge; ignorance of the real nature of the disease, of its cause and of its method of propagation. It is a chilling thought that ignorance under the first two heads has only been dissipated less than half a century ago. Even a medical historian of the standing of Charles Creighton in his *History of Epidemics*, published in 1891–94, considered the plague to be "a soil poison generated out of the products of cadaveric decay." Bacteriology began in 1870, but it was not until 1894 that a Japanese scientist discovered the bacillus of plague, and only thereafter were the dual nature of the disease (bubonic and pneumonic) and its propagation by the rat flea established.

It has to be admitted that we owe our immunity from disasters of plague not only to modern methods of quarantine and port inspection of incoming vessels but also to the merely incidental facts that the black or house rat was displaced in the seventeenth and eighteenth centuries by the brown or sewer rat, which does not breed inside the house, and also that those centuries saw the change from wood and plaster in house construction to the cleaner brick and stone which provided no material in which rats could nest. From the sixth to the eighteenth centuries plague was endemic in Europe, breaking out into fierce epidemics at intervals up to the early eighteenth century.

Ideas of contagion and infection had been current for many centuries though their vagueness but rarely permitted success in combating infectious disease. We moderns, to whom the notions of disease and infection are hardly separable, cannot easily appreciate the mental attitude of earlier centuries when microorganisms were unknown and the wisest men talked of miasmas and for safeguards burnt herbs or carried scented pomanders [Plate 43]. Before Fracastoro (1483–1553) there was no clear exposition of the theory of infection as we understand it. Babylonians, Egyptians, Hebrews, all recognized the existence of infectious disease (as we have noted in earlier pages), but apart from mystic "demons," "hand of a ghost" or "the wrath of the Lord" it does not appear that more than the fact of infection was realized though it is perhaps more than a curiosity that the emblem of the Babylonian god, Nergal, god of pestilence and destruction, was the fly, which we now know to be a disease carrier. The Hebrews appear to have been well aware of the facts of contagion (see Chap. II). Again it is perhaps more than merely curious that in the plague of Ashdod when "the hand of the Lord was heavy upon them of Ashdod and he . . .

smote them with emerods" (1 Sam. v.) we find not only that the plague is identified with bubonic plague ("emerod" is considered to be a corruption of "hæmorrhoid," and to mean a swelling, which is the outstanding symptom of bubonic plague) but that mice are associated with it. The "trespass offering" which the Philistines had to make before they could be healed was "five golden emerods and five golden mice" which were to be "images of your emerods and images of your mice that mar the land." Again the Lord smote the army of Sennacherib (2 Kings xix. 36) in the seventh century B.C. and mice appear, according to Herodotus, in association with this plague. Whether the connection in this and other instances (the mouse god Smintheus was made responsible for pestilence in the *Iliad*) was accidental or not is a question which has not been finally decided. The known association of the rat with plague makes it a question of tantalizing interest.

Although Hippocrates treats epidemic diseases in large and wise spirit (see page 58) he does not appear to possess the idea that they are infectious and most of the Greek medical writers fail in the same way. The atmosphere ('airs," "miasmas," etc.) is held responsible for spread of disease as the only known cause acting everywhere. Other ancient writers of later times recognized the fact of infection but regarded it as a minor cause. All through the Middle Ages, through the horrors of the Black Death, the one prophylactic measure was purification of the atmosphere whether by fire (Pope Clement VI sat between two great fires at Avignon during the Black Death, a not unreasonable proceeding) or by fumigation with incenses and burnt herbs and an endless variety of aromatic essences.

In the sixteenth century the litterateur, scientist and physician, Girolamo Fracastoro "first opened men's eyes to the nature of contagion" (as a contemporary declared), in a work published at Venice in 1546 of which the third book was entitled *De Contagione et Contagiosis Morbis et Curatione*. Up to this time fevers were classed as "ephemeral," "putrid" and "hectic" and ascribed to corruption of the humours. Fracastoro finally disposed of these superficial views and clearly distinguished both causes and varieties of infection. Dr. Singer says that "at the back of all modern views on infectious diseases lies the work of Fracastoro." His book *De Contagione* contains "three contributions of the first importance—a clear statement of the problems of contagion and infection, a recognition of typhus fever and a remarkable pronouncement on the contagiousness of phthisis."—(*Osler*.)   Others before him had expressed somewhat similar ideas but Fracastoro first stated clearly the modern doctrine.   The three varieties of infection recognized once and for all in this genuinely scientific work are: (1) infection by contact (contagion is an infection passing from one individual to another and is the same in him whom receives and in him who gives); (2) infection by indirect means, as by a garment, or fomites (Fracastoro invented this term *fomes* which is still the only term used to describe infected articles); (3) infection at a distance.

Moreover, three centuries before bacteriology he outlined the mechanics of infection in his doctrine of *seminaria*, invisible seeds of contagion, or germs.   Thus he says:

> These seeds are the carriers of the contagion and that they are the first origin of the disease there can be no doubt.
> It may be considered that the force of the disease lies in those seeds since they have the power to propagate and reproduce their own kind.

The conditions of his time undoubtedly helped Fracastoro in his work by providing him with ample material for study. He saw several waves of epidemic disease, including typhus, phthisis, rabies, leprosy and the English sweat.   Venereal disease was first recognized in Italy in his youth about 1494, and his study of it produced that extraordinary poetic work, half romantic and half clinical, published in 1530 and dedicated to a Cardinal, entitled *Syphilis sive Morbus Gallicus*, from which the disease was named.   After the *Regimen Sanitatis Salerni* it is the best-known and most frequently printed medical poem. Its interest to us, apart from the Virgilian graces of its seventy pages of Latin verse, is threefold.   It gave the disease one name instead of the many which then multiplied confusion, it described the symptoms accurately, and thereby distinguished it as a separate disease; and insisted on the virtues of the only two remedies—mercury and guaiacum—which have availed until the discovery of salvarsan, the arsenic compound, in the twentieth century.

It is with a sense of disappointment that we find that, despite the accuracy and clarity of Fracastoro's work on infection, the purely medical methods of combating the great plagues of the sixteenth and seventeenth centuries were no improvement in practice on those of the fourteenth and fifteenth.   Until the germ itself was discovered really effective measures to stamp out the disease were not possible but once the doctrine of contagion was properly laid down it is not unreasonable to expect real effort to prove its efficacy and benefit by it. Perhaps it remained something of a scientific curiosity; it is always difficult for the practical man to believe in the remorseless activity of something unseen. Certainly, with few exceptions, the machinery was inefficient and generally insufficient however harshly at certain times and places segregation was enforced. Notable exceptions are commented on below. Like the poor, plague was always present, and it is probable no town was free from sporadic cases. When the terror struck, i.e. when the mortality rates rose much above the customary, isolation was applied but it was often half hearted and generally too late. Then the flight began from the stricken city and the disease was but carried abroad.

Always plague has followed communications—trade routes, shipping, etc. The great plague of Rome in the second century, described by Galen, was introduced from Syria by the Roman army. The Black Death, perhaps the most appalling visitation of all, was brought from the Near East by a Genoese ship to Messina in 1347, and spread by fugitives all over Sicily and Tuscany by 1348, whence it covered the whole of the rest of Europe. Even Greenland did not escape. There the plague, as Sir Charles Oman has declared, deflected history by wiping out a community which was then in touch with North America and knew the route there one hundred and fifty years before Columbus.

The results in mortality of the Black Death were appalling. Estimates vary from a quarter to more than half of the entire population of Europe for the period 1348–59. According to Guy do Chauliac three-quarters of the people of France died. Germany which suffered relatively lightly is estimated to have lost one million two hundred and forty-four thousand persons.— (*Nohl.*) In England about half the population disappeared, the report from London being that scarcely one in ten survived. In Italy again half the people died, cities like Venice and Florence losing three-quarters of their inhabitants. Boccaccio reports that in Florence with about one hundred and thirty thousand inhabitants more than one hundred thousand died. The consequent misery and horror cannot be adequately described. Boccaccio's own long and dramatic account of the plague as he saw it in the neighbourhood of Florence has often been quoted and need not be repeated here. One poignant paragraph is sufficient to strike the note:

multiplication of minute organisms. In the last great European plague, that of Marseilles and Toulon in 1720, when ninety thousand lives were lost, drastic quarantine prevented further spread.

The plague doctors of Marseilles are represented in many prints garbed in long gowns and masked hoods, carrying tapers, a costume that, queer and even ludicrous as it may seem, is not dissimilar to that necessarily adopted by the twentieth century attendant on pneumonic plague cases. He, too, wears a mask filtering all inhaled air, rubber gloves and long boots and goggles to protect the eyes [Plate 46]. The views of the famous Dr. Mead on sanitation in plague time are referred to in a later page.

The part that medicine has played in the fight against this worst of all man's enemies was, in earlier days, of less importance than that played by hygiene; even now it is overshadowed by bacteriology.

The disease which, after plague, attracted most attention in the medieval world was leprosy. This was, in part, because attention was drawn to it by its description and detailed regulation in the Old Testament and also because of obvious indications of its steady increase. By the sixth century it was spreading through France. Here it was the Church which took action because the authority for action was derived from Holy Writ. Although leprosy is definitely contagious (the lepra bacillus can be transmitted by direct contact as well as by fomites) yet it is less easily transmitted than nearly all other chronic infections, and it is characteristic of the mental attitude of the early Middle Ages that the only public measures adopted in attacking disease were those applied to the disease described in Leviticus xiii. and xiv. However, they had their effect in time in driving home the idea of general contagion.

The first action was the strict limitation of leper movement by the Edict of Lyons in 583. Other ecclesiastical ordinances based on Leviticus followed and a general system of prevention was gradually elaborated. The leper was banished from all social life and with solemn ceremony declared civilly dead, condemned to associate only with fellow sufferers until physically dead. Even so his manner of life was narrowly restricted. He could not go barefooted on the highways, he had to announce his presence by horn or rattle and to wear warning signs on his clothes. Leper-houses and leper-colonies were established which, at the height of the infection, had about twenty thousand occupants. By a rigid system of inspection and exclusion which

PLATE XLV
Scenes in the Great Plague of 1665

The set of woodcuts in this broadside of 1665 or 1666 appeared in various forms, some close copies, for several years after the Great Plague. In the first cut the plague sick receive attention, with a coffin ominously in the foreground: in the second, the rat-catchers, by a most unfortunate ignorance of the source of infection, have turned dog-slayers (*see* page 126): in the third, fourth, sixth and last are scenes of flight by land and water from the stricken city. The remainder show the disposal of the dead.

From Walter G. Bell, " The Great Plague in London in 1665."

PLATE XLV

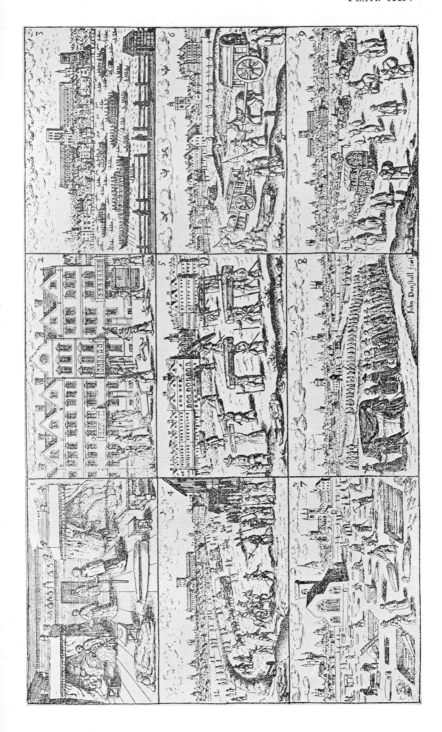

PLATE XLVI

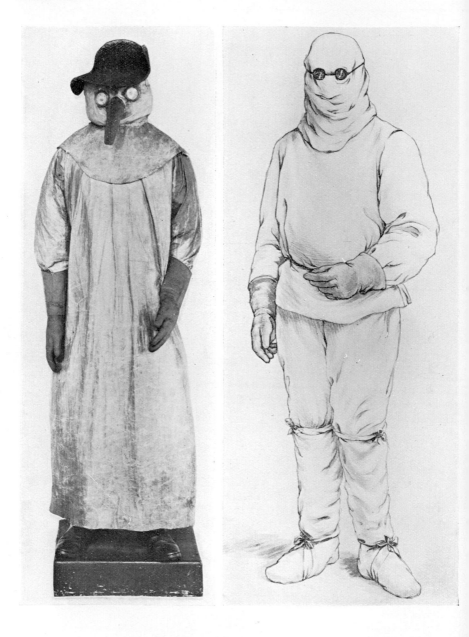

PLATE XLVI

PLAGUE DOCTORS IN THE SEVENTEENTH AND TWENTIETH CENTURIES

By the early seventeenth century it had been clearly recognised that plague infection could and did cling to clothing, and the person and the plague doctor adopted the sufficiently reasonable costume, curious in appearance, shown on the left-hand figure. Protection, though not complete, was probably fairly good, provided cleanliness was maintained. The long peaked nose covering was stuffed with aromatic substances. It was certainly realised that the deadly infection could be projected through the air on moisture from the sick man's breath or cough.

His completely protected modern successor is seen on the right. This was the costume adopted with success by the Japanese in the virulent epidemic of pneumonic plague in Manchuria in 1909–10.

PLATE XLVI

Plague Doctors in the Seventeenth and Twentieth Centuries

By the early seventeenth century it had been clearly recognised that plague infection could and did cling to clothing, and the person and the plague doctor adopted the sufficiently reasonable costume, curious in appearance, shown on the left-hand figure. Protection, though not complete, was probably fairly good, provided cleanliness was maintained. The long peaked nose covering was stuffed with aromatic substances. It was certainly realised that the deadly infection could be projected through the air on moisture from the sick man's breath or cough.

His completely-protected modern successor is seen on the right. This was the costume adopted with success by the Japanese in the virulent epidemic of pneumonic plague in Manchuria in 1909-10.

in the end became non-ecclesiastic, Europe was practically freed in the course of centuries from this contagion. It is not unknown in modern times in certain coastal districts of Northern Europe, but otherwise is extinct in the West although it remains common in the East, in South Africa and in the tropics. An average of six hundred patients are segregated on Robben Island near Capetown. The modern treatment by injection with chaulmoogra oil and its derivatives has produced a number of cases of cure. Chaulmoogra has been known as an antidote since 1500 B.C., but its use has always been limited by the bad effects on the liver when given medicinally in the large doses necessary.

Like leprosy and the plague other diseases, which in earlier times were serious enemies of the Western world, have retreated to other parts and are now regarded as essentially tropical. These include malaria, dysentery and typhus fever. The second cannot be brought within the scope of this very brief survey and the third is referred to in Chapter XVI. The first was, until the late nineteenth century, extremely common in most districts of England. References to it as ague are found in very many sixteenth, seventeenth and eighteenth century writers. The great Sydenham owed something of his renown to his treatise on the subject. The epidemics of ague of the sixteenth to eighteenth centuries were due, particularly in England, to ill-drained swamps where the malaria mosquito bred freely and where it continued to breed freely for over three centuries. Dr. Singer points out that in St. Thomas's Hospital, London, between 1850 and 1860 more than one-twentieth of the patients were cases of ague, a disease which we now rightly regard as tropical. Drainage works carried out in London and the country after that date resulted in the disappearance of the disease, and a careful search for a native case of malaria at the beginning of the twentieth century produced only one example.

Malaria has been a constant enemy from very early times. In the varying forms which we know it was a scourge in Hippocrates' day (as we have noted) and some authorities are disposed to credit it with an important part in the destruction of the ancient Greek civilization. Although it was banished from this country eighty or more years ago it is still endemic in many parts of Europe. It is only fifty years since the blood parasite which causes the disease was discovered by Laveran and little over thirty since Sir Ronald Ross proved its transmission by one variety of mosquito (*anopheles*). Sir Patrick Manson, who

K

first made the suggestion that led to the incrimination of the mosquito, confirmed the conclusions of Ross by experiment in the malaria districts of the Campagna. The double life-cycle of the parasite in the stomach and salivary gland of the mosquito and in human blood is so elaborate that its determination is a biological achievement of a very high order. Since the cause of the disease has been established preventive measures against the insect pest responsible have made large areas of the tropics healthy and inhabitable to a degree beyond all possibility forty years ago.

The ever famous campaign of General Gorgas against mosquito borne disease in the Panama Canal area has shown that hygienic organization can control devastating disease. The outstanding triumph at Panama was the elimination of yellow fever, a virulent epidemic disease transmitted by another mosquito (*stegomya*). As a result it is now restricted to the West coast of Africa and a few places in South America.

A sixteenth-century medical professor of Leyden, Peter Forest, included in his *Observations* another epidemic disease from which, unfortunately, none of the modern world is yet free. We quote Dr. Withington's translation:

Epidemic catarrh at Delft, 1580: At the end of June and throughout July epidemic catarrhs spread *publice ac catervatim* throughout the neighbourhood. They were of sudden onset, very contagious, accompanied with fever, and inflammation of the throat and lungs, with hoarseness and coughing, so that whole families were suddenly struck down thereby; but the disease was not very dangerous, and many easily escaped by immediate bleeding and gentle purgatives, though in some it passed on to peri-pneumonia, and others had severe pleurisy. This febrile epidemic raged not only here but throughout France and Germany, and came to us *afflatu quodam* from those regions. After July it decreased, but revived in the autumn when many recovered without bleeding; but in winter the catarrhs were worse, with bloody sputa and pleuritic pains.

In this we are to recognize the protean disease called by the Italians of the seventeenth century "the influence" because they ascribed it to the influence of the stars. The French name "La Grippe" appears about 1743. Huxham described it in England as "influenza" in 1750. Partly because of its protean nature (a medical authority states that it occurs in so many various forms that it is often difficult to say whether features of an individual case are complications or belong to the disease proper), and also because of the difficulty in earlier days of distinguishing it from other "catarrhs" and bronchial affections, we do not hear as much of it in records before the sixteenth and seventeenth centuries as the severity of later epidemics might lead us to expect. After the epidemic of 1580 described above, there was one in the seventeenth century, six in the eighteenth and four in the nineteenth up to 1847, and then a long interval of quiescence. Its bacteriological cause is not yet known, although several microbes have been found guilty of association with it. Of its vicious capacities the two world epidemics of 1889-90 and 1918-19, particularly the latter, gave cruel evidence. In fifteen months from October, 1889, the disease traversed the entire globe and it was estimated that from thirty to ninety per cent. of the various populations was attacked. In seven countries of Europe alone in 1918-19 there died one million four hundred and forty thousand and those mainly persons of robust health and youth. If the six million deaths in India be added the total exceeds all those killed in the whole four years of the Great War. Over three thousand died in London in one week in October, 1918. Europe has seen nothing worse since the Black Death nearly six centuries back.

The horrors of large-scale infection need not be laboured; it remains that disease, and epidemic disease in particular, has always been and yet is the worst enemy of man. And so having very briefly surveyed this long story of pity and terror, of achievement and failure, we will resume our sequence in the centuries we have hastened over and turn to the relatively quiet days of the seventeenth century where we see the beginnings of a scientific enquiry that was to do much for the true enlivening of medical thought. This science first manifests itself in a spirit of superior curiosity such as attracted together those eager minds that founded the Royal Society.

CHAPTER XI

It is a remarkable fact that the space of a century, which mankind has accepted as a convenient measurement of time, usually answers perfectly to that artificial limit by assuming a particular quality or colour in the mind of the student. It is impossible to confuse the fifteenth century with the sixteenth century, the seventeenth with the eighteenth. In tracing the development of medicine and the evolution of ideas of hygiene, it will be well if in considering our next period we can fix on some great figure or movement to sum up the quality of the time.

The special virtue or quality of the seventeenth century was the birth of modern physiology, and it is usual to begin accounts of this epoch by recording the discovery of the circulation of the blood by William Harvey.

For our present purpose it will, perhaps, be better to forsake strict chronology for a few years, and to note a profoundly important weekly event that was taking place in London about the year 1645, "sometimes at Dr. Goddard's lodgings, sometimes at the Mitre in Wood Street hard by." A few young men met weekly "at a certain day and hour, under a certain penalty, and a weekly contribution for the charge of experiments, with certain rules agreed upon amongst us." In these words does John Wallis, himself afterwards a great mathematician, record the inception of the first concerted movement in England towards the study and discussion of Natural Philosophy. "We barred," he continues, "all discourses of divinity, of State-affairs, and of news (other than what concerned our business of Philosophy), confining ourselves to philosophical inquiries, and such as related thereunto; as Physick, Anatomy, Geometry, Astronomy, Navigation, Staticks, Mechanicks, and Natural Experiments."

The other chief members of this small private club were John Wilkins, afterwards Bishop of Chester; Jonathan Goddard, a noted physician, still remembered by his remedy, Goddard's

Drops; George Ent, a physician, afterwards knighted, and friend and executor of the great Harvey; Francis Glisson, who was to write a classic work on the rickets; Charles Scarbrough, also later on to be knighted, and to attend Charles II in his last illness; and Christopher Merrett, who became first librarian of the collection of books which Harvey gave to the College of Physicians. It will be observed that the bias of this company was medical. But as yet its members were young (the average age being thirty-four), and they met each week to discuss scientific subjects in a new way. The meetings were removed, soon after, to the Bull's Head in Cheapside, or to Gresham College.

In 1648 the man who was probably the most versatile of the little band was appointed Warden of Wadham College, Oxford. This was John Wilkins, a man of immense learning and great originality of mind, who besides being interested in a possibly habitable world in the moon, and in a universal language, made experiments while he was at Wadham in the art of flying. Let us listen for a moment to what a young disciple of his, Robert Hooke, wrote of this man a quarter of a century later:

If these my first Labours shall be any wayes useful to inquiring men, I must attribute the incouragement and promotion of them to a very *Reverend* and *Learned Person*, of whom this ought in justice to be said, *That there is scarce any one Invention, which this Nation has produc'd in our Age, but it has some way or other been set forward by his assistance.* My reader, I believe, will quickly ghess, that it is *Dr. Wilkins* that I mean. He is indeed a man born for the *good* of *mankind*, and for the *honour* of his *Country*. In the *sweetness* of whose *behaviour*, in the *calmness* of his *mind*, in the *unbounded goodness* of his *heart*, we have an evident Instance, what the true and the *primitive unpassionate Religion* was, before it was *sowred* by particular *Factions*. In a word, his *Zeal* has been so *constant* and *effectual* in advancing all good and profitable *Arts*, that as one of the Antient *Romans* said of *Scipio, That he thanked God that he was a* Roman; *because whereever* Scipio *had been born, there had been the seat of the Empire of the world:* So may I thank God, that *Dr. Wilkins* was an *Englishman*, for whereever he had lived, there had been the chief Seat of *generous Knowledge* and *true Philosophy*. To the truth of this, there are so many worthy men living that will subscribe, that I am confident, what I have here said, will not be look'd upon, by any ingenious Reader, as a *Panegyrick*, but only as a *real testimony*.

It is not surprising that young men, wearying of the theological disputes of their fathers and the dust of civil war, grouped themselves round this remarkable man in order to discuss subjects more directly of importance to the progress of mankind. The meetings begun at the Mitre were continued in Dr. Wilkins's lodgings at Wadham, or at Dr. Petty's lodgings in Oxford "because of the conveniences we had there (being the house of an apothecary) to view, and make use of, drugs and other like matters, as there was occasion."

Perhaps no group of names possesses more meaning for the birth of the modern spirit in science than the names of Dr. Wilkins's young men. "The principal and most constant of them" were Seth Ward, first an astronomer, and afterwards Bishop of Exeter, and then of Salisbury; the Honourable Robert Boyle, our first great chemist; William (afterwards Sir William) Petty, soon to be Cromwell's First Physician to the Army in Ireland, and ultimately our first political economist; Matthew Wren, son of the Laudian Bishop of Ely, and cousin to the architect of St. Paul's; John Wallis; Jonathan Goddard; Thomas Willis, a physician who was occupied in researches on the brain and nervous system; Ralph Bathurst, a physician who became also Dean of Wells; Laurence Rook, an astronomer who died at the early age of thirty-nine; and the greatest genius of them all, the young anatomist Christopher Wren, who had come up to Wadham presumably, as Sir Lawrence Weaver points out, to be under the influence of Wilkins. The object of these men was "a free way of reasoning", and

> "their first Purpose was no more than only the Satisfaction of breathing a freer Air, and of conversing in Quiet one with another, without being ingag'd in the Passions and Madness of that dismal Age. . . . To have been always tossing about some *Theological Question*, would have been, to have made that their private Diversion, the Excess of which they themselves dislik'd in the publick: To have been eternally musing on *Civil Business*, and the Distresses of their Country, was too melancholy a Reflexion: It was *Nature* alone, which could pleasantly entertain them in that Estate."
>
> "And," continues their first historian, Bishop Sprat, "from the Institution of that *Assembly*, it had been enough if no other Advantage had come but this: That by this means there was a Race of young Men provided against the next Age, whose Minds receiving from them their first Impressions of *sober* and *generous Knowledge*, were invincibly arm'd against all the Inchantments of *Enthusiasm*".

They took the whole of Natural Science for their field, and gradually moulded their meetings into a clearing-house for scientific information. Meanwhile it is of importance for the purpose of this book to note that those members of the circle whose interests were medical were constantly busy dissecting or performing experiments on living animals, and that there grew up an Oxford school of physiology which, in a golden period of fifty years, entirely changed the course of medical knowledge, and turned its stream from the arid desert of medieval theory into the rich fields of experiment. For the moment it will be sufficient to remember that among the names of these young Oxford physiologists were Christopher Wren, Robert Boyle, Robert Hooke, Richard Lower, John Mayow, Francis Glisson, and Thomas Willis.

The meetings were continued at Oxford till about the year 1658, by which time certain of the members had removed to the larger world of London. The Restoration came in 1660, and it will ever be to the honour of a king not always credited with the more dignified qualities of kingship that in 1662 Charles II consolidated the status of the society by giving it a Royal Charter. Thus was born The Royal Society of London.

It cannot be too clearly emphasized that it was by the method of experiment and the gradual registering of facts that the new Society was to be useful to mankind. There was to be no dogmatizing, but only the acceptance of data, until such time as any new fact or evidence arrived to disturb or set aside the first conclusion. This is the true method of science, and it was in England in the seventeenth century that the theory first became the accepted instrument of knowledge. The new Baconian philosophy was bearing its fruit in action, and it is significant that when John Evelyn, the diarist, came to design a symbolical frontispiece for the First Edition of Sprat's *History of the Royal Society*, 1667, the figure of Francis Bacon was prominent in it [Plate 48].

But now, having set the stage for the modern era of medical science in England, we must leave it for a few moments for Padua, to witness there an interlude which exhibits in a surprising flash the birth of the modern method of research. The middle ages are dead, and there is no "*Vive le moyen âge.*"

Sanctorius Sanctorius (1561–1636) was Professor of Theoretical Medicine at Padua. The great Galileo was also at that university, and it was clearly from Galileo's influence that Sanctorius conceived the idea of applying exact measurement to the hitherto elusive functions of the body.

Sanctorius constructed a weighing-chair, a chair attached to a balance, by which he could contrast the difference in his own weight before and after a meal, before and after sleep, and under other varying conditions. He distinguished between sensible and insensible perspiration. Sensible perspiration comprised the several normal evacuations of the body, but by insensible perspiration he designated the processes of which we are unconscious, and to estimate these by variations in weight Sanctorius spent the best part of thirty years in his weighing-chair. At times he even slept in it.

In one of his aphorisms he says:

> " That is the most proper time of Eating, wherein the Body comes to some healthful Standard, as it enjoyed the Day before, when empty: But that *Apollo* himself cannot find out, without the Ballance."

This method of research does seem rather to preclude a sense of humour, and one wonders a little what the poets would say to it.

But Sanctorius, by his devotion, laid the foundation of the modern science of metabolism, and it is in recent times that his work has borne most fruit, so that we have an interesting example of an isolated train of research, instinct with the modern spirit, considerably written about in the century following the author's death, but without recognition of its practical importance, and ultimately coming to life again in our own day. He was well aware that he had initiated a new method of inquiry in medicine, as will be seen from Sir Michael Foster's translation of Sanctorius' preface to his book:

> It is a new and unheard of thing in Medicine that anyone should be able to arrive at an exact measurement of insensible perspiration. Nor has anyone either Philosopher or Physician dared to attack this part of medical inquiry. I am indeed the first to make the trial, and unless I am mistaken I have by reasoning and by the experience of thirty years brought this branch of science to perfection, which I judged more advisable than to describe all the details of my inquiry.

Sanctorius published the results of his researches in a book, called *De Statica Medicina*, at Venice, in 1614. It consists of nearly five hundred short aphorisms, divided under the headings of Insensible Perspiration, Air and Water, Meats and Drink, Sleep and Watching, Exercise and Rest, Affections of the Mind, and what the seventeenth century called Venery. It is from the English translation of John Quincy (Fourth Edition, London, 1728) that we give a few examples of Sanctorius' aphorisms. Some have been chosen to exhibit the results of his experiments

PLATE XLVII

SIGNATURES OF CHARLES II AND THE DUKE OF YORK IN THE CHARTER BOOK OF THE ROYAL SOCIETY

On the 9th of January, 1665, The Royal Society received their Charter, and the King and the Duke of York signed their names at the head of the Charter-Book. The King signed himself "Founder," and the Duke of York "Fellow". The Duke of Albemarle (George Monk) entered his name at the same time. The president, Lord Brouncker, so often mentioned by Pepys, then kissed the King's hand in recognition of the honour conferred on the Society. At the meeting of the Society on the 11th of January, the book was produced.

Pepys happened to be at Whitehall on the day of the signing, and his account brings us very near to the event; Jan. 9: "Up and walked to Whitehall, it still being a brave frost, and I in perfect good health, blessed be God! In my way saw a woman that broke her thigh, in her heels slipping up with the frosty street. To the Duke, and there did our usual works. Here I saw the Royal Society bring their new book, wherein is nobly writ their charter and laws, and comes to be signed by the Duke of York as a Fellow; and all the Fellows' hands are to be entered there, and he as a mountaineer; and the King hath put his with the word Founder. Thence I to Westminster, to my barber's, and found occasion to see Jane, but in presence of her mistress, and so could not speak to her of her failing me yesterday; and then to the Swan to Herbert's girl, and lost time a little with her, and so took coach, and to my Lord Crew's and dined with him, who received me with the greatest respect that could be."

From "The Universal History of the World".

TITLE-PAGE OF THE FIRST EDITION OF NEWTON'S "PRINCIPIA," 1687

The book was published by the Royal Society, and Pepys, as President, licensed it for publication. He had been elected President on the 1st of December, 1684, and his association with one of the two or three most important books in the history of science emphasizes that aspect of him which is furthest from the popular view of this great public official. In his later life he corresponded with Newton.

British Museum.

PLATE XLVII

SIGNATURES OF CHARLES II AND THE DUKE OF YORK IN THE CHARTER BOOK OF THE ROYAL SOCIETY

On the 9th of January, 1665, The Royal Society received their Charter, and the King and the Duke of York signed their names at the head of the Charter Book. The King signed himself "Founder" and the Duke of York "Fellow". The Duke of Albemarle (George Monk) entered his name at the same time. The president, Lord Brouncker, so often mentioned by Pepys, then kissed the King's hand in recognition of the honour conferred on the Society. At the meeting of the Society on the 11th of January, the book was produced.

Pepys happened to be at Whitehall on the day of the signing, and his account brings us very near to the event: Jan. 9: "Up and walked to Whitehall, it still being a brave frost, and I in perfect good health, blessed be God! In my way saw a woman that broke her thigh, in her heels slipping up with the frosty street. To the Duke, and there did our usual worke. Here I saw the Royal Society bring their new book, wherein is nobly writ their charter and laws, and comes to be signed by the Duke of York as a Fellow; and all the Fellows' hands are to be entered there, and lie as a monument; and the King hath put his with the word Founder. Thence I to Westminster, to my barber's, and found occasion to see Jane, but in presence of her mistress, and so could not speak to her of her failing me yesterday, and then to the Swan to Herbert's girl, and lost time a little with her, and so took coach, and to my Lord Crew's and dined with him, who received me with the greatest respect that could be".

From " The Universal History of the World ".

TITLE-PAGE OF THE FIRST EDITION OF NEWTON'S "PRINCIPIA," 1687

The book was published by the Royal Society, and Pepys, as President, licenced it for publication. He had been elected President on the 1st of December, 1684, and his association with one of the two or three most important books in the history of science emphasizes that aspect of him which is farthest from the popular view of this great public official. In his later life he corresponded with Newton.

British Museum.

PLATE XLVII

Charles R
founder

James
Fellow

PHILOSOPHIÆ
NATURALIS
PRINCIPIA
MATHEMATICA.

Autore *J S. NEWTON,* Trin. Coll. Cantab. Soc. Matheseos
Professore *Lucasiano,* & Societatis Regalis Sodali.

IMPRIMATUR·
S. PEPYS, *Reg. Soc.* PRÆSES.
Julii 5. 1686*i*

LONDINI,
Jussu *Societatis Regiæ* ac Typis *Josephi Streater.* Prostant Vena-
les apud *Sam. Smith* ad insignia *Principis Walliæ* in Cœmiterio
D. *Pauli,* aliosq; nonnullos Bibliopolas. *Anno* MDCLXXXVII.

PLATE XLVIII

PLATE XLVIII

FRONTISPIECE OF THE FIRST EDITION OF SPRAT'S "HISTORY
OF THE ROYAL SOCIETY ", 1667

This plate was designed by John Evelyn, the Diarist, and was
engraved by Wenceslaus Hollar, and was prefixed to some copies of
the First Edition. In the centre is a bust of Charles II. On the left
is the first President, Lord Brouncker, and on the right Francis Bacon.
At the top of the picture are the arms of The Royal Society.

Sprat's book was first published in 1667, and there were subsequent
editions in 1702, 1722, and 1724. Cowley contributed an Ode to The
Royal Society, and the book may be read to-day as a fine example of
English prose just settling down to the classic virility of the age of
Dryden. Thomas Sprat (1635–1713) was Bishop of Rochester and
Dean of Westminster.

in insensible perspiration, but others are of more general interest in connection with questions of health. All are the work of an acute and probing mind.

Sect. 1

OF INSENSIBLE PERSPIRATION, AS IT APPEARS BY WEIGHT

Aph. 1.   If there daily be an Addition of what is wanting, and a Substraction of what abounds, in due Quantity and Quality, lost Health may be restor'd, and the present preserved.

Aph. 2.   If a *Physician*, who has the Care of another's Health, is acquainted only with the sensible Supplies and Evacuations, and knows nothing of the Waste that is daily made by insensible Perspiration, he will only deceive his Patient, and never cure him.

Aph. 3.   He only who knows how much, and when the Body does more or less insensibly perspire, will be able to discern, when, and what is to be added or taken away, either for the Recovery or Preservation of Health.

Aph. 4.   Insensible Perspiration alone, discharges much more than all the servile Evacuations together.

Aph. 5.   Insensible Perspiration is either made by the Pores of the Body, which is all over perspirable, and cover'd with a Skin like a Net; or it is performed by Respiration through the Mouth, which usually, in the Space of one Day, amounts to about the Quantity of half a Pound, as may plainly be made appear by breathing upon a Glass.

Aph. 6.   If eight Pounds of Meat and Drink are taken in one Day, the Quantity that usually goes off by insensible Perspiration in that Time, is five Pounds.

Aph. 9.   If the Body encreases beyond its usual Weight, without eating or drinking more than customary, there must either be a Retention of some of the sensible Excrement, or an Obstruction of the perspirable Matter.

Aph. 17.   A Person may certainly conclude himself in a State of Health, if upon ascending a Precipice he finds himself more lightsome than before.

Aph. 21.   That Perspiration which is beneficial, and most clears the Body of superfluous Matter, is not what goes off with Sweat, but that insensible Steam, or Vapour, which in Winter Time exhales to about the Quantity of fifty Ounces in the Space of one natural Day.

These are all extraordinarily modern statements for the year 1614 when Avicenna was still being taught in the medical schools of Europe. It is a great pity that Sanctorius did not record the methods but only the results of his experiments.

Sect. 1.

Aph. 55. Too thick Apparel hinders Perspiration, by wasting the Spirits.

Aph. 123. A Person may happen upon such a Way of living, even when he takes no Care about it, as may preserve him to a good old Age.

Aph. 139. (Of the Plague). Very few of the Wealthier people are cured by Medicines, but a great many of the poorer Sort recover without them.

Sect. 4.

OF SLEEP AND WATCHING

Aph. 2. With seven Hours sleep the Body insensibly perspires, and without any Trouble, twice as much as when awake.

Aph. 25. Changing a Bed occasions disturbed Sleep, and lessens Perspiration; for an unaccustomed Place, although better than before, disturbes both the Body and Mind.

If Sanctorius could eliminate the boredom of the weighing-chair he would be Nature's best philosopher.

While it is true that Bacon was the turning influence in this country that led to the clearing of men's minds, and to the forsaking of the dogmas and mysticism of the Middle Ages, for the real world of experiment and the correlation of knowledge, it is now necessary to go back from the London and Oxford of the Restoration, and to record that in 1578 there had been born at Folkestone, just seventeen years after Bacon himself had been born, a man who was not only one day to be Bacon's physician, but who was to do for physiology, and by means of it for medicine, as much by actual experiment and proof as Bacon did for natural science by precept.

William Harvey (1578–1657) was the discoverer of the circulation of the blood, and it is for this reason that no biographical fact concerning his life is without interest. He was born of prosperous yeoman stock at Folkestone in 1578 and went to school at Canterbury. From there he went to Cambridge, where at Caius he graduated in Arts, and then, choosing the profession of medicine, he proceeded at the age of twenty-one to study it at the famous medical school at Padua.

Through Harvey's selection at Padua, chance or destiny brought him to the well-spring of modern anatomy, and to the clue which set his mind on the track of his shining discovery.

Vesalius, Professor of Anatomy at Padua, had laboured there

for five years, and by the publication of his *Fabrica* (1543) became the true founder of modern anatomy and physiology. When Vesalius left Padua his duties were entrusted for a short time to a deputy, Matheus Realdus Columbus, but in 1551 Vesalius's chair was given to Gabrielus Faloppius, his devoted pupil. Faloppius in turn was succeeded in 1565 by his own pupil Hieronymus Fabricius of Aquapendente, and it was during this excellent man's reign as professor of anatomy that Harvey came to study medicine at Padua. It will thus be seen that the young Harvey, as were very many other young men, was in daily contact with the great Vesalian tradition. The Englishman from Kent alone carried it to its exquisite logical conclusion.

Harvey, then, came to Padua, where he found the legend of Vesalius in active flower, and it is worth remembering at this point that his master, Fabricius, had paid special attention to the valves of the veins, and four years before Harvey was born had discovered, in 1574, what he later called, in his book *De Venarum Ostiolis*, 1603, "the little doors of the veins" [see Plate 50].

Harvey remained at Padua for four years, till in 1602, he received the degree of Doctor of Medicine and returned to England. He settled in London, became a Fellow of the College of Physicians in 1607, and was appointed physician to St. Bartholomew's Hospital in 1609.

In 1615 Harvey was appointed Lumleian Lecturer by the College of Physicians, an appointment which entailed public lectures on subjects connected with the human body. In April, 1616, he began to give these lectures, and from his own manuscript notes for them, which are still in existence, it is known that at the very commencement, during the second day lecture, he began to bring forward new views on the movements of the blood and heart. He had certainly made good use of the thirteen years since he left Padua, for by dissection and vivisection, inference and reasoning, and by the final touch of that fire which we call genius, he had been enabled to arrive at a point of knowledge which definitely divides the new world of physiology from the old.

But even now he "studied to be quiet", and was in no hurry. He went on for some years attending his patients and lecturing and proving by experiment the truth of his theory. It is known that he dissected at least eighty species of animals, and by his system of research and observation and checking and reasoning he came to that position of impregnable argument which at last he published to the world in his book *Exercitatio Anatomica de Motu Cordis et Sanguinis in Animalibus* (Frankfurt, 1628).

Why, it may be asked, had not the circulation of the blood been discovered before, and what exactly is the circulation of the blood, and what led Harvey to the special study of the subject?

From early times it had been observed that in some sense the blood moved. Aristotle had had his teaching concerning the movement of the blood, and Galen had elaborated a theory about it which lasted as a false sign-post for centuries. But all this was mere vagueness about some minor desultory and local ebb and flow. Towards the end of the Middle Ages some light began gradually to break, and Vesalius, Servetus, Cæsalpinus, Columbus, and Fabricius had all made some contribution to the subject.

The circulation of the blood had not been discovered before Harvey's time, because the method of physiological observation by vivisection, dissection, and experiment was in its childhood. It was the genius of Harvey that seized on the new instrument, moulded it to his needs, and by long years of applying it to the motions of the heart and blood at the same time perfected a method and proved a theory.

We tread on perilous and debated ground if we try to fix too dogmatically on what it was that first led Harvey to his discovery, but it is at least allowable to repeat that his master Fabricius of Aquapendente published a book on the Valves of the Veins in 1603, and it is difficult, in the light of a conversation which Boyle had with Harvey late in life, not to believe that it was the teaching of his old master at Padua that first set Harvey musing on the motion of the blood. This is what Boyle says:

> And I remember that when I asked our famous *Harvey*, in the only Discourse I had with him, (which was but a while before he dyed) What were the things that induc'd him to think of a *Circulation of the Blood*? He answer'd me, that when he took notice that the Valves in the Veins of so many several Parts of the Body, were so Plac'd that they gave free passage to the Blood Towards the Heart, but oppos'd the passage of the Venal Blood the Contrary way: He was invited to imagine, that so Provident a Cause as Nature had not Plac'd so many Valves without Design: and no Design seem'd more probable, than That, since the Blood could not well, because of the interposing Valves, be sent by the Veins to the Limbs; it should be Sent through the Arteries, and Return through the Veins, whose Valves did not oppose its course that way.— (*Disquisition About the Final Causes of Things*, 1688.)

PLATE XLIX

PADUA UNIVERSITY: FRONT OF THE BUILDING CALLED THE GYMNASIUM

This shows a portion of the University as Harvey knew it, and it may be seen, little altered, to-day. In the rooms within this building he listened to those lectures which set him on the road to the basic discovery of modern physiology. The engraving is dated 1623. Note the shops on the ground floor in the front portion of the University building.

PLATE XLIX

GYMNASIVM PATAVINVM

PLATE L

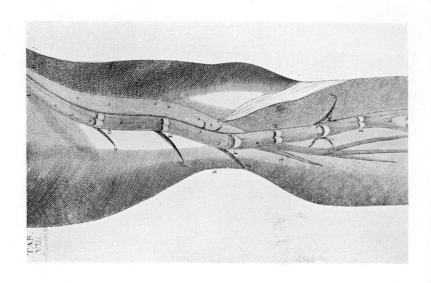

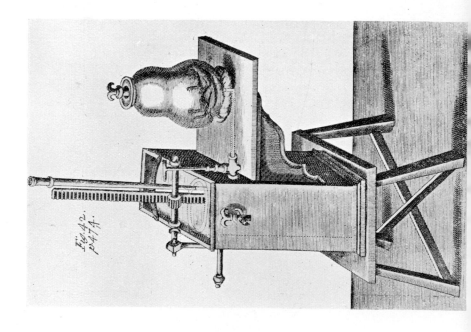

It is not the function of this book to demonstrate physiological processes, but rather to point to the current ideas concerning them, and to emphasize the influence of those ideas on fresh achievements in medicine. But it must be explained that what Harvey proved was that the heart is a pump, a muscular pump, that forces the blood into its circulatory course, and that to support his theory he also used the quantitative argument, that the smallness of the capacity of the vessels of the heart makes it impossible that it can be other than the *same* blood which goes and returns, and goes and returns again. To this must be added the words of Sir Michael Foster:

> The essential feature of Harvey's new view was that the blood through the body was the same blood, coursing again and again through the body, passing from arteries to veins in the tissues, and from veins to arteries through the lungs, heart, suffering changes in the substance and pores of the tissues, changes in the substance and pores of the lungs. The new theory of the circulation made for the first time possible true conceptions of the nutrition of the body, it cleared the way for the chemical appreciation of the uses of the blood, it afforded a basis which had not existed before for an understanding of how the life of any part, its continued existence and its power to do what it has to do in the body, is carried on by the help of the blood. And in this perhaps, more than its being a true explanation of the special problem of the heart and the blood vessels, lies its vast importance.

After the publication of his great discovery Harvey turned his attention to the problems of embryology and generation, and published in 1651 his *Exercitatio de Generatione Animalium*. In this he got probably as far as he could without the aid of the microscope, but he does not attain to the finality of the *De Motu Cordis*.

During these years England had been distracted by civil war. Harvey was physician to Charles I, and was present at the battle of Edgehill, where he was in charge of the two young princes, and retired with them to the shelter of a hedge, "and tooke out of his pockett a booke and read; but he had not read very long before a bullet of a great gun grazed on the ground neare him, which made him remove his station." He was with the Court at Oxford, and remained there for three years, and it is amusing to remember, now that the needs and fame of St. Bartholomew's Hospital are daily before our eyes, that that great foundation, while Harvey was absent, was in half a mind to dispense with her famous physician because he "hath withdrawn himself from his charge, and is retired to the party in arms against the Parliament."

For the rest it need only be said that Harvey was a munificent patron of learning, and a devoted son of the College of Physicians. While he was yet alive he built for the College a noble library, with a great parlour underneath, and filled the library with rare books, and he made over to the College his estate at Burmarsh in Kent.

The publication of Harvey's book on the Circulation caused tremendous controversy, and he had his enemies and detractors, as he has had in even more recent times. Their favourite method was to ascribe the knowledge of the circulation either to the ancients, or to one or other of the earlier Italian anatomists.

We cannot conclude this account of Harvey better than by quoting a noble sentence from Joseph Glanvill's *Plus Ultra: or, The Progress and Advancement of Knowledge since the Days of Aristotle*, 1668. Glanvill was the writer in one of whose other books, *The Vanity of Dogmatizing*, Matthew Arnold found the story of the Scholar Gipsy. But here is what Glanvill, his late contemporary, says of Harvey: "And therefore here I am no otherwise concerned, but to have *Justice* for that Excellent Man: And the World hath now done *right* to his *Memory*, *Death* having overcome that *Envy* which *dogs living Virtue* to the *Grave;* and his *Name* rests quietly in the Arms of *Glory*, while the *Pretensions* of his *Rivals* are *creeping* into *darkness* and *oblivion*."

CHAPTER XII

MEANWHILE on the Continent there were springing up two main influences or branches of seventeenth-century medical thought. They came into being contemporaneously with the enormous advances in physiology in this century, and it is interesting to observe one of them at first trying to come to some terms with the thought of the Middle Ages, while the other struck out on an entirely new line. For the sake of perspective, it will be more helpful here to try to consider both movements as current modes of thought rather than by a string of names to leave an imperfect impression of masters and waning disciples.

The first, the more conservative tendency, was that known by the name of the Iatro-chemical School. It had its origin in the work of Paracelsus (1493–1541), whom we met in a previous chapter. But now, early in the seventeenth century, the strongly chemical element in the teaching of Paracelsus was taken up, refined, and expanded into a more rational system by Jean Baptiste van Helmont (1577–1644), who was born at Brussels in 1577. He practised as a physician at Vilvorde, near Brussels, and it is to his thought, tempered by the influence of the Vesalian school of physiology, that we owe the inception of a new science, that of the chemistry of physiology. He evolved a theory of ferments, by which he explained the inner chemical workings of the body, especially of the functions of digestion, and he uses finally the vivid analogy of "the kitchens of the several members," and refers to the fact that a "ferment innate in each place cooks its food for itself."—(*Foster.*) "In the language of to-day," says Sir Michael Foster, "all the tissues live upon the common blood, and the power of assimilation lies in the tissue itself."

But Helmont adapted to all this the relics of medievalism by also carrying forward the Paracelsean presiding genius, the Archæus, or series of archæi, who were inherent in and presided over the various ferments of the body. A disturbance of the particular archæus caused that archæus to disturb the ferments over which it presided, and illness was the result. The whole doctrine was at once a harking back to the mystical and a reaching forward to modernity.

Then again, Helmont at a leap, by his discovery of a new element, and by his naming it *Gas*, introduced a new principle to the structure, and a new word to the language, of modern science. His "gas" was carbon dioxide or carbonic acid gas.

He was not so illuminated, however, when he gave the name *Blas* to his Archæus or series of archæi. The whole system was presided over by a sensitive motive soul (*anima sensitiva motivaque*) which resided in the pit of the stomach. The profound importance of Helmont is that he began to have some real apprehension of the chemical processes of the body, especially of the functions of digestion, nutrition, and assimilation.

It is obvious that matters could not stand at the half mystical and half chemical stage at which Helmont left them. Like Paracelsus, Helmont in turn had his disciple, and his name was François de la Boe (1614–72), usually known as Franciscus Sylvius. He was born at Hanover, and in 1658 he became Professor of Medicine at Leyden. Sylvius had the advantage over Helmont in that he was acquainted with all the recent advances in anatomy and physiology, and with that admirable equipment he proceeded to carry on the interpretation of the fermentative or chemical processes of the body. He dropped entirely Helmont's mystical tendencies, and stepped forward as the expositor of a purely chemical explanation of natural functions. This was his great merit. He especially carried forward the theory of digestion as a matter of chemistry. He made no great original discoveries, but he was a persistent and inspiring teacher, and he influenced pupils who were more original investigators than he was himself, and we quote from Sir Michael Foster his translation of the admirable portrait of Sylvius drawn by one of his pupils, the great Niels Stensen. We have in the last sentence perhaps the greatest tribute that can be paid to any teacher:

> No one as yet, so far as I know, has so joined Chemistry to Anatomy as to have clearly and distinctly explained, not by deductions from the doctrines of the schools but by following up the indications of Nature, in what respects muscle tendon and bone agree and in what they differ.

My most eminent teacher Sylvius has laboured in this way with happy results, in respect to the humours of our body; and, if I remember rightly, I have often listened to him while he led by the same spirit of inquiry discoursed also concerning the nature of tendons and bones. But that eminent man although he has done much in this branch of knowledge is, lest he might seem to sacrifice the public weal to his own glory, in the habit of daily assuring his pupils that he has not been able to accomplish everything. Hence he expounds, in the shape of views and speculations, matters concerning which he has not yet arrived at a clear and definite result, and thus he stimulates others to inquiry, supplying them at the same time with problems to begin with.

The other school of thought is known as the Iatro-mathematical School. It had its chief inspiration in the work of Giovanni Alphonso Borelli (1608–79). He was born at Naples, and became Professor of Mathematics, first at Messina, then at Pisa, and then at Messina again. At Pisa he worked side by side, usually in friendship, with Marcello Malpighi, the Professor of the Institutes of Medicine, that profound and immortal investigator with the microscope. It was an association probably as fruitful as any in the whole history of science.

Borelli was primarily a mathematician, and began as a follower of the great Galileo, but he eventually became interested in the application of mathematical principles to the mechanics of animal motion, and ultimately to the explanation of problems of physiology. In this direction he carried out research after research with that seemingly profound ease which is at intervals seen attendant on great genius when it contends with hitherto unsolved problems.

Borelli's name belongs to physiology rather than to medicine, but he must have his place in any account of medical thought because he was followed by a school of medical disciples who applied his mathematical methods to the secrets of the human body, first usefully, but in the end almost to the point of sterility. The human body became likened to a machine, and any function of it could be explained by some analogy in mechanics. Here, indeed, was a doctrine to sweep away the last relics of medievalism, and in that it did this, it partook of the nature of a cleansing process. The greatness of Borelli and his vast services to science, however, cannot be demonstrated in a work not primarily concerned with physiology.

L

in the seventeenth century is largely the story of physiology, we can do no more here than indicate that a new physiological world was now brought before men's eyes, but ourselves remember all the time that what most interests us at the moment is what the discovery of the microscope meant for the doctrines and investigation of contagion.

We have seen that Fracastoro (1484–1553) in his book, *De Contagione* (1546), had enunciated the first really modern theory of contagion.

Between the time of Fracastoro and the middle of our seventeenth century the medical world was from time to time attracted by and curious about the diverse and yet loosely allied phenomena of very small living creatures: vermicles, living atoms, bodikins, and animalcules, and the processes of corruption, putrefaction and fermentation. The magnifying glass had begun to bring to men's eyes some premonition of those mysteries which the microscope was to write large on their consciousness. Such easily discovered subjects as the mites in cheese, the maggots in decaying meat, and even the homely object-lesson of the flea, began to engage the scientific mind, and there is little doubt that by 1650 there was abroad something of that curious spontaneity of kindred ideas in different places of which the history of science from time to time affords instances. But nobody had as yet seen through the microscope those little creatures in the blood on which a new science was one day to be based. One may merely say that the scientific world was prepared to see them.

At this point we are tempted to follow for a few moments a rather dangerous episode (for the experts differ) in the history of microscopy before we proceed to the five great pioneers of the science, especially as its effects can be illustrated by an English writer whose connection with the subject has not, as far as we are aware, been noticed in any detail before.

In 1656 there was plague at Naples and Genoa. It spread to Rome, and it there became one of the score of objects of scientific inquiry on the part of an excessively learned Jesuit priest, Athanasius Kircher (1602–80). He was a man who took all learning for his province, one of those profound dilettanti who filled with their works the shelves of seventeenth century libraries. But Kircher was accustomed to use the microscope, and when he examined with its aid the blood of those who had the plague he was astonished to see "an innumerable Swarm of Worms." Modern microscopists have decided that Kircher did not see what are now known as bacteria, but either blood corpuscles or perhaps some larger species of micro-organism. But he wrote a book [Plate 51], and published it a couple of years later, *Scrutinium Physico-Medicum Pestis* (1658), and in many passages arrives at a very creditable theory of bacteria. The following two passages, for the translation of which we are indebted to the writer's friend, Mr. Arnold M. Muirhead, express vividly Kircher's surprise at what he saw:

P. 141 : Little worms that cause the plague are very small and imperceptible.

I have shown above that the plague commonly has animate life. For once a sick man has become infected with the ravages of the plague, he is soon subject to a remarkable corruption, which (as I have shown in the same passage) is the most suitable of all for the generation of worms. But these worms which cause the plague are so small, thin, and elusive, that they cheat every attempt at identification by the naked eye, and, if they were not actually seen with the aid of a very powerful microscope, one would say also that they were mere particles. Moreover, they continually multiply in such numbers that one cannot count them: and inasmuch as they have been conceived and generated out of corruption, so they are readily expelled along with sweat through all the passages and pores of the body. Being also set in motion by the slightest disturbance of air, they are disturbed just as particles of dust by a sunray in a dark place: then flowing out of the body, they next cling most tenaciously to whatever they meet with, working their way deeper into any interstices they find.

The corrupt blood of those suffering from fevers has shown me that the process is actually as I have described it. For in one or two hours after blood-letting, I have found the blood so full of worms as almost to render even me astonished, and as a result I am to this extent persuaded that in man, both the living and the dead body breeds innumerable albeit imperceptible worms. And here the saying of Job is much to the point: " I have said to Corruption, 'Thou art my Father': to the Worm, 'Thou art my Mother and my Sister'."

Therefore one infected with the corruption of the plague not only expels a veritable germination of worms through the aforesaid passages of the body, but his dead body also expels these little worms into the air because heat no longer exists in the corruption, and they are then driven into any neighbouring bodies. Since these worms are so very tenacious and elusive, they soon work their way into the inmost fabric of linen and garments, and are there nourished in the same kind of vaporous moisture from which they have come. And this is the primary and chief breeding-ground of all infection, as I shall show.

P. 42: *All corruption generates worms spontaneously and of its own substance.*

It is so definitely established that air, water, and earth, abound in innumerable worms that it can even be demonstrated to the eye. It was also previously known that worms abound in diseased bodies, but it was not known, until after the wonderful invention of the microscope, that all corruption swarms with innumerable worms that are imperceptible to the naked eye. Even I would never have believed this had I not proved it by frequent experiments over a number of years.

The story of Kircher and his "vermicles" can now be further followed in an episode in the life of a harassed contemporary of his over in England. The two men were bound by nothing in common but the somewhat tenuous link of the worm. The following account of him is offered not for its scientific interest, but it is in some ways not unamusing, and perhaps the hero of it has never hitherto received credit for being one of the first, if not the first, of English writers on the Germ Theory.

Marchmont Needham was one of the earliest of English journalists. He was also at times a free-lance physician, and his one medical book [Plate 51], *Medela Medicinae* (1665), is the reason of his appearance here. But he would be a very picturesque subject for a modern biographer, as he possessed to a remarkable degree that mental adaptability which has, in the progress of journalism, been so useful an ally to the pen, and he was a pioneer in an age when it could be exercised to the last fullstop. Unfortunately the rewards in Needham's day were quite inadequate, for slit ears were then much commoner than glittering prizes. Anthony à Wood, his contemporary, wrote an account of his life with all that art which hardly conceals art, which Anthony had ever at his command when the subject did not meet with his approval.

Needham was born at Burford, in Oxfordshire, in 1620, and like many great men of that period he proceeded to All Souls' College. He was usher at Merchant Taylors' School, and later an Under Clerk at Gray's Inn. He studied medicine too, and by 1645 was practising it.

But previously to that he had started on a journalistic career, and in 1643 a paper called *Mercurius Britannicus* began to appear, in which Marchmont "made weekly sport by railing at all that was noble . . . wherein his endeavours were to sacrifice the fame of some lord, or person of quality, nay, of the

King himself." From which it will be seen that in 1643 he was not on the side of the King. He was arrested twice, in 1645 and 1646.

Then follows a pretty scene when in 1647 he sought the King's presence at Hampton Court, and "then and there knelt before him, and desired forgiveness for what he had written against him and his cause; which being readily granted, he kissed his Majesty's hand, and soon after wrote *Mercurius Pragmaticus*. This, too, was a weekly paper, "which being very witty, satyrical against the Presbyterians, and full of loyalty, made him known to, and admired by the bravadoes and wits of those times." At last he was "narrowly sought after" by the Parliamentarians, and though for a time he "skulk'd at Minster Lovel, near Burford," he was caught and imprisoned in Newgate.

In three months he was out and at it again, and no one knew better than Marchmont that it was quite time to change sides once more, and over he went to the Commonwealth. His vehicle this time was *Mercurius Politicus*, which began in 1650, and went on for ten years. About this time he seems to have made that invaluable psychological discovery that "numbers of inconsiderable persons . . . have a strange presumption that all must needs be true that is in print." Cromwell made him also editor of the *Public Intelligencer*.

Things began to be a little uncomfortable in the year 1660, and he fled to Holland. But not to despair: for shortly afterwards, "for money given to an hungry courtier," he obtained pardon under the Great Seal, and returned to England. He then practised medicine till his death, with only an occasional pamphleteering foray. He died in 1678. "He was," says Wood, "a person endowed with quick natural parts, was a good humanitian, poet, and boon droll."

In 1664 he was writing what was to be his one medical work, apart from two prefaces to other men's books. *Medela Medicinae* is an interesting book, full of fine strong epithets, nor is he unaware of the value of alliteration. It is an attack on the old Scholastic methods, a plea for a return to observation and experience from the blind following of ancient writers. "I would not detract from them . . . but 'tis necessary to be a little brisk in expression, because the world is apt to dote on old authors." And brisk he is, though with an amount of learning, quotation, and pertinent observation surprising in so busy and harassed a publicist. He possesses real insight, and begins scientifically enough by drawing from Graunt's recently published *Bills of Mortality*. He has a high admiration for Bacon, is very fond of Dr. Willis, and quotes much from Boyle. Again and again he shows himself a modern, and pleads for a chemical rather than a scholastic solution. He is a great opponent of phlebotomy, and desires a new, more experimental, materia medica.

But the most exciting and creditable thing about his book is Chapter V. Kircher's *Scrutinium Pestis* had fallen into Needham's hands (he refers to the author as "the famous Jesuite, now living at *Rome*"), and he gives an account of Kircher's experiments with the microscope, with much real apprehension of what Kircher's discovery of "vermicles" might mean. Needham's definition of a microscope is worth quoting: "An Instrument so made, and fitted with glasses at each end, as that the smallest thing will be represented by it in so considerable a bigness, that the frame and composure of its Parts may be discerned."

Much of Needham's chapter is a skilful patchwork of translated or paraphrased passages from Kircher, and as the object of these few pages is to illustrate Kircher rather than Needham, we have chosen in the following extracts only those which do represent in Caroline English what Kircher wrote in contemporary Latin. Needham gives also a translation of Kircher's account of six experiments on the breeding of worms in putrefying matter, but for these we have not space here.

It should be remembered that we have in the following passages a very early contribution in the English language to the literature of the Germ Theory. It may well be objected that by lifting passages from their context one can prove anything. But here we are not particularly trying to prove a thesis, and Needham himself was not setting out to prove, in the light of the scientific knowledge of to-day, what Kircher had or had not seen, on that particular afternoon in Rome, through his microscope. We merely take the opportunity of observing the impression made by Kircher's work on a competent mind long before the official evolution of the Germ Theory. And Needham himself for his insight in an age of better equipped scientific minds than his was, may as well at last have his due.

Here are his versions from Kircher:

The Design of this Book is, to treat of the *Pestilence*, its Original, Causes, Signes, and Cure; The occasion of his writing was the strange Nature of the Pestilence which raged at *Naples* and *Genoa*,

TITLE-PAGE OF KIRCHER'S "SCRUTINIUM PESTIS", ROME, 1658

In this book Athanasius Kircher, a learned Jesuit priest, announced that he had seen living worms in the blood of plague patients through his microscope, and evolved a theory of "living contagion" in which he anticipated the modern science of bacteriology.

TITLE-PAGE OF MARCHMONT NEEDHAM'S "MEDELA MEDICINAE", LONDON, 1665

Marchmont Needham, a figure in the history of English journalism, came across Kircher's *Scrutinium Pestis* two or three years after its publication, and with considerable acumen wrote an account of Kircher's theory of living contagion, which he published as the fifth chapter of this book. He translated or paraphrased passages from Kircher, and to Needham credit should be given for apprehending with his quick wit what more learned men in England were slower in taking up. A good example of the crowded title-pages of the seventeenth century. They must at all costs catch the reader's attention. Needham does not describe himself as a Doctor of Medicine, which he was not, but vaguely as "Med. Londinens", a Physician of London.

PLATE LI

ATHANASII KIRCHERI E SOC. IESV
SCRVTINIVM
PHYSICO-MEDICVM

Contagiosæ Luis, quæ PESTIS dicitur.

QVO

Origo, causæ, signa, prognostica Pestis, nec non insolentes
malignantis Naturæ effectus, qui statis temporibus,
cælestium influxuum virtute & efficacia, tum
in Elementis, tum in epidemiis hominum
animantiumque morbis elucescunt;
una cum Antidotario Prophylactico remediorum
Antidota nova doctrina in
lucem eruuntur.

A D
ALEXANDRVM VII.
PONT. OPT. MAX.

ROMÆ, Typis Mascardi. MDCLVIII.
SVPERIORVM PERMISSV.

MEDELA MEDICINÆ.

A P L E A

For the Free Profession, and a Reno-
vation of the Art of

PHYSICK,

Out of the Noblest and most
Authentick Writers.

Shewing

{
The Publick Advantage of its Liberty.
The Disadvantage that comes to the Publick by any
sort of Physicians, imposing upon the Studies and
Practice of others.
The Alteration of Diseases from their old State and
Condition.
The Causes of that Alteration.
The Insufficiency and Uselesness of meer *Scholastick*
Methods and *Medicines*, with a necessity of new.
}

Tending to the Rescue of Mankind from the Tyranny of Diseases; and
of Physicians themselves, from the *Pedantism* of old *Authors*
and present *Dictators*.

The Author, M. N. Med. Londinens.

Medice, Cura Teipsum.

LONDON, Printed for *Richard Lownds* at the *White Lion* in *S. Pauls* Church-yard, neer the Little North-door. 1665.

PLATE LII

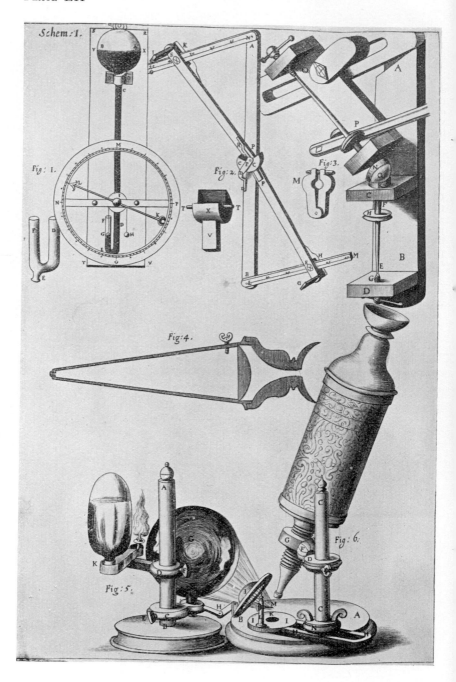

PLATE LII

HOOKE'S MICROSCOPE

This plate is reproduced from Hooke's *Micrographia*, London, 1665, and it was with such an instrument as this that Hooke made his discovery of the cells in cork. The diagrams above the microscope are of an apparatus which Hooke invented to measure the refraction of various liquids. On the left may be seen a condenser for concentrating light, either from the sun or from a wick lamp.

"The *Microscope*", says Hooke, "which for the most part I made use of, was shap'd much like the sixth Figure of the first *Scheme*, the Tube being for the most part not above six or seven inches long, though, by reason it had four Drawers, it could very much be lengthened, as occasion required; this was contriv'd with three Glasses: a small Object Glass . . . a thinner Eye Glass . . . and a very deep one . . .; this I made use of only when I had occasion to see much of an Object at once; the middle glass conveying a very great company of radiating pencils, which would go another way, and throwing them upon the deep Eye Glass. But when ever I had occasion to examine the small parts of a Body more accurately, I took out the middle Glass, and only made use of one Eye Glass with the Object Glass, for always the fewer the Refractions are, the more bright and clear the Object appears. And therefore, 'tis not to be doubted, but could we make a *Microscope* to have only one refraction, it would, *ceteris paribus*, far excel any other that had a greater number ".

Anno 1656, and from thence flew to *Rome*, the Symptoms whereof were such as agreed not with the old Descriptions, and baffled all the old Antidotes and Cordials, and puzzled the Physicians in all their Consultations about the Causes and Cure of it: Which *Kircherus* considering, and pondering various Causes, at length pitched upon those *Effluviums*, *Atoms*, *Corpuscles*, or *Ferments*, which . . . do continually flow forth of all gross Bodies through the Air, whereby even the said gross Bodies do touch and take with one another, according as they are capable to receive Impressions from each other, through the working and counter-working of these Intermedial flitting Atoms or Bodikins, which when they issue from Contagious Bodies, impart somewhat of their own Natural Venom, and improve it, wheresoever they fix; and He thereupon concluded, that some such little contagious bodies as these, carried through the Air, and insinuating themselves into the Bodies of Men, did, by their pernicious Ferment, induce a putredinous pestilent disposition in the Humors, and consequently, the Pestilence it self, where Nature had not strength enough to oppose and hinder the operation of its Fermental Force and Power.

In the above passage we have already arrived at a very creditable theory of bacterial infection. In the following sentences we are taken a step farther and observe in Kircher a definite prescience of bacteria:

But that which most remarkably touches the Point in hand, is, that he introduceth a new *Paradox*, (as himself calls it) into the world, *viz.* That the Contagion of the Pestilence was at that time conveyed abroad, not only by the volatility of such Effluviums, Atoms, and Corpuscles, as are *Inanimate*, but by such also as were *Animated*, living Creatures, and were a sort of *Invisible Worms* or Vermicles. This might seem strange at the first Report, and not to be believed, unless that which is not to be perceived commonly by Sight, may by help of Art be presented to the Eye, and then there is no disputing against Sense.

This that Author undertakes to do, (of which more by and by) and saith, That these Animated Effluviums are constituted of indiscernable Animated Corpuscles, it doth appear by the multitude of Worms which are wont to issue out of one and the same Body; of which some are so big that they are presently seen, the rest remain in an undiscernable state of Magnitude, yet multiplyed in so great a number, as the numberless Corpuscles or Particles are, of which the Effluvium doth consist; and being exceeding subtile, thin, and light, they plie to and fro, no otherwise than Atoms do, with the least puff or motion of the Air:

And he saith, These Worms are so fine, that they insinuate themselves, not only into Clothes, Ropes, and Linen, but into other Bodies less Porous, as Cork, Wood, Bones; yea, into those which are least Porous and most compact, as metals, money, &c. Of this he in another place tells us, they had daily Experience in the Plague-time, at *Naples* and *Rome*, where no money was received in Payment, but what was first well soaked and washed in

Vinegar, if it came from any Infected Place; and he believed, nothing could resist the penetration but Diamonds only, because of their polished Superficies, and unconquerable hardness.

By such *Animated Effluviums* as these, *Cardan* saith, the great Plague that fell out in his time at Milan was raised, which unpeopled that great City, not only the Air being filled with them, but the very dust of the Earth animated into such kind of Vermicles.

Here is a passage which is of interest as it displays the novelty of the microscope to the seventeenth century reader:

But if you would know, how these Vermicles come to be made visible, which are of so minute a Magnitude, and so subtil a Substance; the same Author tells us, the visibility is attained by the Instrument called a Microscope. These things (saith he) may perhaps seem Paradoxes to the Reader, but when he shall, as I have done, by Experiments made the space of many years, by the help of most exquisite Microscopes, throughly see with his own Eyes, then I suppose, he will not only believe these things to be so, but instructed by Experience, be ready to attest the Truth of what I have said.

In the following extract Kircher, through his interpreter Needham, is not so satisfactory from the point of view of modern science, but it is instructive as displaying the mind of the early microscopist trying to grapple with the difficulties of the situation:

The learned Author gives so much Light to this as hath convinced me, by manifold *Experiments*, which because they are the best kind of Arguments; and the clearing of this being of very great importance to the practice of Physick, I will set down all, but make them as short as I can. Before he comes to *Experiments*, he lays down this for a Position; *Omne Putridum, ex se & sua Natura generare Vermes:* i.e. *That every thing which is Putrid, doth of it self, and by its own Nature, generate Worms:* whereupon he thus reasoneth. Whereas all generation consists in what is hot and moist, according to the Philosopher's determination, a twofold Corruption may here be considered; the one Natural, the other specially adventitious or beside Nature, which properly is wont to be called Putrefaction.

I say therefore, that there is no living thing which is not lyable to Putrefaction, even as the Philosopher [Aristotle] himself affirms. For the understanding whereof, it is to be noted, that no living thing can be generated out of what is formally Putrid. But whenas that which is putrefied, being a mixt Body, is, by separation of impure parts from the pure, resolved into its own Elements, and whereas the pure Parts natural to the mixt Body being mingled with the putrid, are agitated by heat; and forasmuch as Nature always intends the best hence it comes to pass, that the external heat works the prepared matter, not into any thing which is of an Excrementitious Nature, but thrusts forth the purer Parts of the Mixt Body into somewhat that is animated; and this is the only Cause of the Original of Animals out of Putrefaction.

Moreover, whereas Philosophers are wont commonly to say, that some Animals are generated out of meer Putrefaction alone, that is true, if we conceive the whole putrefaction of a mixt Body to be performed under one Action, but because no mixt Body is so corrupted, but that some of the purer Parts natural to it do remain; therefore when these purer Parts become Tinctured with in an ill fuliginous quality through the putrefying of the Excrementitious Parts, hence it falls out, that the said purer Parts being agitated by external heat, do thrust forth an Off-spring of Animals, of the same Nature with the Excrementitious Parts which gave the Tincture.

Again, there is no kind of Plant which doth not out of slime or mucous Matter, generate a certain Worm peculiar to it self; which secret is in these last Times discovered by the *Microscope*, and will be more experimented. Yea, Vinegar, Milk, the Blood of men in Fevers, are perceived to be full of Worms, although not to be discerned by an eye that is not armed with that Instrument.

Our last quotation is a short one of which we have already given a modern translation, but we repeat it so that the two may be compared, and that it may be seen how closely on the whole Needham reproduced Kircher:

All Bodies are subject to Putrefaction, and out of Putrefaction spring Animals. And that Worms of bigness visible arise out of putrid Bodies, is a matter known to All; but that all putrid Bodies should abound with an innumerable Swarm of Worms not to be perceived by the eye of it self, is a matter that was never known till the admired Invention of the *Microscope*: which I my self could never have believed, unless I had found it true by many years experience.

To sum up, Kircher, whatever he saw through his microscope, arrived by remarkable flashes of insight or prescience, at a basis for the modern germ theory. Here is one of the occasions where the idea is greater than the fact of the moment, and where, for once, the end justifies the means. To Needham also must be given the credit of seizing, in the true journalistic spirit, on the importance of Kircher's theory, and of presenting it, all hot from the press, to his readers, probably before his more academic brethren in England had awakened to the situation.

There now follow five great names of men who, gifted with he delight of taking infinite pains, established the new science of microscopy on a firm basis, backed up by a series of books illustrated with engraved plates of wonderful beauty and accuracy. We have now left the vague regions of Kircher, and enter the terrain of exact science.

The researches of these men belong chiefly to the departments either of vegetable or animal or human histology and physiology, but it is essential to make grateful mention of these pioneers, because without them the science of bacteriology would be unknown, and medicine might still be groping, sightless, in the infinite dark.

To begin, then, in our own country, there is first Robert Hooke (1635–1703). He was Curator of Experiments to the Royal Society, and one of the most remarkable and versatile men of his age. For some reason or other, possibly because he was overshadowed by his great junior Newton, justice has hardly been done to his memory till lately, when Dr. R. T. Gunther, of Magdalen College, edited and published *The Life and Work of Robert Hooke* (2 vols., Oxford, 1929). "Had he," writes Dr. Gunther, "been a countryman of Galileo or Goethe, the whole world would now be ringing with his fame." If the reader will look into these two volumes he will be astounded that any man could possess such powers of invention, or be at home in every branch of scientific research. He was an architect as well, and was Surveyor to the City of London after the Great Fire. "Before I leave this towne," writes his friend Aubrey to Anthony à Wood in 1689, "I will gett of him a catalogue of what he hath wrote; and as much of his inventions as I can. But they are many hundreds; he believes not fewer than a thousand."

It is always well, if we can, to carry away some scent or colour of a man's period, so let us stay for a moment to read also what Aubrey, his contemporary and friend, says about Hooke:

> He is but of midling stature, something crooked, pale faced, and his face but little belowe, but his head is lardge; his eie full and popping, and not quick; a grey eie. He haz a delicate head of haire, browne, and of an excellent moist curle. He is and ever was very temperate, and moderate in dyet, etc. . . . As he is of prodigious inventive head, so is a person of great vertue and goodness. . . . He is certainly the greatest mechanick this day in the world.

A vivid portrait, and more arresting than can be written by any modern pen. We are giving these details of Hooke because it is to him that the scientific world owes the foundation of the

Cell Theory, which, in Dr. Gunther's fine phrase, "became the greatest biological generalization of all ages."

In the year 1665 Hooke published the beautiful small folio volume called *Micrographia : or Some Physiological Descriptions of Minute Bodies Made by Magnifying Glasses. With Observations and Inquiries Thereupon.* It is from this book that we may date the beginnings of the Cell Theory, on which the whole of modern biology rests. Hooke discovered what he himself named "cells" in the structure of cork, and it was for the science of a later day to expand this working discovery to the whole realm of histology. Schleiden (1804–81) and Schwann (1810–82) early in the nineteenth century developed the Cell Theory as one of the greatest instruments of modern research. But here is Hooke's description of his great experiment:

> I took a good clear piece of Cork, and with a Pen-knife sharpen'd as keen as a Razor, I cut a piece of it off, and thereby left the surface of it exceeding smooth, then examining it very diligently with a *Microscope*, me thought I could perceive it to appear a little porous; but I could not so plainly distinguish them, as to be sure that they were Pores, much less what Figure they were of: But judging from the lightness and yielding quality of the Cork, that certainly the texture could not be so curious, but that possibly, if I could use some further diligence, I might find it to be discernable with a *Microscope*, I with the same sharp Pen-knife, cut off from the former smooth surface an exceeding thin piece of it, and placing it on a black object Plate, because it was it self a white body, and casting the light on it with a deep *plano-convex Glass*, I could exceeding plainly perceive it to be all perforated and porous, much like a Honey-comb, but that the pores of it were not regular; yet it was not unlike a Honey-comb in these particulars.
>
> First, in that it had a very little solid substance, in comparison of the empty cavity that was contain'd between, as does more manifestly appear by the Figure A and B of the XI. *Scheme*, for the *Interstitia*, or walls (as I may so call them) or partitions of those pores were neer as thin in proportion to their pores, as those thin films of Wax in a Honey-comb (which enclose and constitute the *sexangular cells*) are to theirs [Plate 53].
>
> Next, in that these pores, or cells, were not very deep, but consisted of a great many little Boxes, separated out of one continued long pore, by certain *Diaphragms*, as is visible in the Figure B, which represents a sight of those pores split the long-ways.
>
> I no sooner discern'd these (which were indeed the first *microscopical* pores I ever saw, and perhaps, that were ever seen, for I had not met with any Writer or Person that had made any mention of them before this) but me thought I had with the discovery of them, presently hinted to me the true and intelligible reason of all the Phaenomena of Cork.

particularly matter. The important fact is that he lived to the age of ninety-one, and spent the greater part of his working-life among his microscopes, and subjected to them every conceivable small object in the world of nature that came to his hand. Nothing escaped him. He made his own microscopes, and ground his own glasses and mounted them. We might note here that both Leeuwenhoek and Malpighi preferred on the whole to use a single-lens microscope, and that with the simplest apparatus the greatest discoveries were made. There seems little doubt that in the grinding of lenses Leeuwenhoek was an artist of the first rank.

He appears to have had no scientific method, except that he was by nature possessed of the best of scientific methods; he used his eyes and exercised his brain with the method and insight of a genius. He went on through the long years at Delft examining everything in a leisurely way, and sending letters, describing what he saw, to the Royal Society. Here again we see the Royal Society acting as the great clearing-house of knowledge. To them at the age of forty he was introduced in a letter by Regnier de Graaf, the physiologist, who sent them an account of some of Leeuwenhoek's observations. Thereafter for the rest of his life Leeuwenhoek sent them constant communications announcing his discoveries. He corresponded also, but on a much smaller scale, with the Paris Academy of Sciences. He became known for what he was, a very distinguished man. The Directors of the East India Company sent him specimens. Peter the Great called on him. There is an incidental reference to him in the *Philosophical Transactions* for 1683, which shows in a charming way how everyone knew of his interests and activities. Dr. Frederick Slare, writing of an epidemic, where animals were infected, remarks: "I wish Mr. Leewenhoeck had been present at some of the *dissections* of these infected *Animals*, I am perswaded He would have discovered some strange *Insect* or other in them."

We now reach the central fact of the theme of this chapter. In the year 1683, or perhaps earlier, Leeuwenhoek first saw bacteria, and in 1683 he published drawings of them in the *Philosophical Transactions*. About the year 1675 he discovered protozoa in water, and the discovery was published in the *Philosophical Transactions* in 1677. Professor Clifford Dobell remarks that this letter may "be regarded as the first page in the history of protozoölogy."

Let us quote, too, another sentence from Professor Clifford

PLATE LIII

THE CELLS IN CORK

In this plate (from *Micrographia*, 1665) Hooke illustrates for the first time cells in a vegetable structure; and by his discovery lays the foundation for the Cell Theory which was to be developed to such great ends by Schwann and Schleiden, and later by Virchow, in the nineteenth century. Hooke cut sections of cork thin enough to permit light to pass through them and observed the two aspects of the cells which he shows (see page 157). In the following passage Hooke seems to apprehend that he was only on the threshold of further discoveries concerning the life of the cell:

"Now, though I have with great diligence endeavoured to find whether there be any such thing in those Microscopical pores of Wood or Piths, as the Valves in the heart, veins, and other passages of Animals, that open and give passage to the contain'd fluid juices one way, and shut themselves, and impede the passage of such liquors back again; yet have I not hitherto been able to say anything positive in it, though me thinks, it seems very probable, that Nature has in these passages, as well as in those of Animal bodies, very many appropriated Instruments and contrivances whereby to bring her designs and end to pass, which 'tis not improbable, but that some diligent Observer, if help'd with better Microscopes, may in time detect."

PLATE LIII
The Cells in Cork

In this plate (from *Micrographia*, 1665) Hooke illustrates for the first time cells in a vegetable structure, and by his discovery lays the foundation for the Cell Theory which was to be developed to such great ends by Schwann and Schleiden, and later by Virchow, in the nineteenth century. Hooke cut sections of cork thin enough to permit light to pass through them and observed the two aspects of the cells which he shows (*see* page 157). In the following passage Hooke seems to apprehend that he was only on the threshold of further discoveries concerning the life of the cell:

"Now, though I have with great diligence endeavoured to find whether there be any such thing in those *Microscopical* pores of Wood or Piths, as the *Valves* in the heart, veins, and other passages of Animals, that open and give passage to the contain'd fluid juices one way, and shut themselves, and impede the passage of such liquors back again, yet have I not hitherto been able to say anything positive in it; though me thinks, it seems very probable, that Nature has in these passages, as well as in those of Animal bodies, very many appropriated Instruments and contrivances, whereby to bring her designs and end to pass, which 'tis not improbable, but that some diligent Observer, if help'd with better *Microscopes*, may in time detect".

PLATE LIII

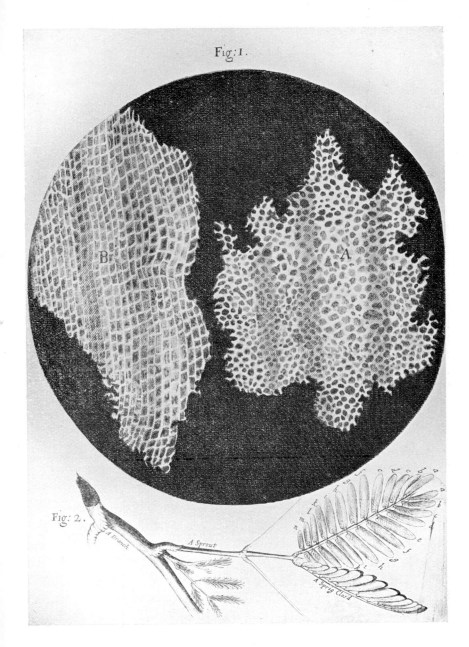

Fig: 1.

Fig: 2.

PLATE LIV

HERMANNI BOERHAAVE
SERMO ACADEMICUS
DE COMPARANDO CERTO
IN PHYSICIS.

LUGDUNI BATAVORUM,
Apud PETRUM VANDER Aa, Bibliopolam.
MDCCXV.

PLATE LIV
Boerhaave Lecturing

Hermann Boerhaave, Professor of Medicine at Leyden, was the greatest power and influence in medicine in Europe in the early eighteenth century. Here he may be seen delivering the oration at the end of his year as Rector of the University of Leyden. The subject is the Means of Arriving at Truth in the Physical Sciences. In this picture the great dignity of the academical world of Boerhaave's time is well conveyed. *De Comparando Certo in Physicis* was published in 1725.

Dobell which vividly gives to Leeuwenhoek his due place in the world of medical science: "He was the first bacteriologist and the first protozoölogist, and he created bacteriology and protozoölogy out of nothing."

What in other ways Leeuwenhoek did with the microscope it is hardly possible even to summarize here. His labours were so vast, and extended over so many years, that the study of them would be the work of a trained specialist. He made investigations into the composition of articles of diet, and is thus an early food chemist. He was interested in the subject of insensible perspiration. He opposed the doctrine, which was prevalent in those days and till very long after, of the spontaneous generation of small animals.

Leeuwenhoek was the first to describe the spermatozoa which, however, were not actually his discovery. He demonstrated and described the capillary circulation which had been discovered by Malpighi. His observations were made on the tadpole, and his communication on the subject he sent to the Royal Society, though they did not publish it. "Herewith I again send you some of my trifling observations." Here finally Harvey's work on the circulation was made complete. Leeuwenhoek gave the first full account of the red blood-corpuscles (1674), though they were discovered by his countryman Swammerdam in 1658.

Leeuwenhoek was the first man to *see* the complete circulation of the blood which Harvey had described and proved. For some time Leeuwenhoek could not hit on the animal which could for this special purpose be completely observed through the microscope. He tried and failed with the combs of cocks, the ears of white rabbits, the wings of bats, but was finally successful with the tadpole. Here is his description of what no man had seen before:

> Upon examining the tail of this creature, a sight presented itself, more delightful than any that my eyes had ever beheld; for here I discovered more than fifty circulations of the blood, in different places, while the animal lay quiet in the water, and I could bring it before the microscope to my wish. For I saw, not only that the blood in many places was conveyed through exceedingly minute vessels, from the middle of the tail towards the edges, but that each of these vessels had a curve, or turning, and carried the blood back towards the middle of the tail, in order to be again conveyed to the heart. Hereby it plainly appeared to me, that the blood-vessels I now saw in this animal, and which bear the names of arteries and veins, are, in fact, one and the

M

same, that is to say, that they are properly termed arteries so long as they convey the blood to the farthest extremities of its vessels, and veins when they bring it back towards the heart.—(*Hoole's Translation*, 1798.)

In the following passage we hear Leeuwenhoek making a general defence of his discoveries. It is of value, also, as giving some idea of the wonder and enthusiasm felt by these early microscopists:

I have often heard, that many persons dispute the truth of what I advance in my writings, saying that my narrations concerning animalcules, or minute living creatures, are merely of my own invention. And, it seems, some persons in France have even ventured to assert, that those are not living creatures, which I describe as discoverable to our sight, and alledge, that after water has been boiled, those particles in it which I pronounce to be animalcules will be still observed to move. The contrary of this, however, I have demonstrated to many eminent men, and I will be so bold to say, that those gentlemen who hold this language, have not attained to a degree of proficiency to observe such objects truly.

For my own part, I will not scruple to assert that I can clearly place before my eye the smallest species of those animalcules concerning which I now write, and can as plainly see them endued with life, as with the naked eye we behold small flies, or gnats sporting in the open air, though these animalcules are more than a million of degrees less than a large grain of sand. For I not only behold their motions in all directions, but I also see them turn about, remain still, and sometimes expire; and the larger kinds of them I as plainly perceive running along, as we do mice with the naked eye. Nay, I see some of them open their mouths, and move the organs or parts within them; and I have discovered hairs at the mouths of some of these species, though they were some thousand degrees less than a grain of sand.—(*Hoole's Translation*, 1798.)

The last of our group is another Hollander, Jan Swammerdam (1637–80). He was born at Amsterdam, the son of a naturalist, and became a physician. He died at the early age of forty-three, and towards the end of his life became the victim of religious melancholy, and in him we could observe, if we had the space, the struggle between religion and science, not in this case in tribunal or consistory, but in a man's own mind.

Swammerdam made important researches on the volume of the heart and on muscular action. He discovered the red blood-corpuscles in 1658, and like Leeuwenhoek opposed the doctrine of spontaneous generation which was to cause so much contention among scientists later on, and even down to the time of

Pasteur. But it was by his great and enthusiastic work on the comparative anatomy and life histories of small insects that he helped to build up the new science of observation of minute structures and tissues.

The lessons taught by the work of these early microscopists did not wholly bear fruit till the nineteenth century, but it must not be forgotten that while Hooke is examining his piece of cork, or Grew the leaf of a tree, or Malpighi the structure of the lung, or Swammerdam a bee's wing, or Leeuwenhoek the tartarization from teeth, the method of investigation is the same, and that these men laid the foundation of what would one day be the profoundly important sciences of biology, physiology, histology, and bacteriology.

CHAPTER XIV

A BASIS OF MODERN PNEUMO-THERAPY: FIRST RESEARCHES IN BREATHING

ANY ACCOUNT of medicine in the seventeenth century must necessarily trespass continually on the borderland of physiology, because during this golden period the history of medicine is largely the history of physiology. However anxious a writer may be to exclude the subject of physiology from his book it becomes impossible during this century to do so entirely. Harvey, by his profound discovery, makes it clear to us (though not perhaps entirely clear to himself or his contemporaries) that no further progress in medicine could be made till the secret of the circulation was solved.

But there was another unanswered riddle that equally obstructed the way to further real progress in the treatment of disease, and this was the problem of why we breathe, and what happens to the air that we do breathe. It began to be answered in the seventeenth century.

The indefatigable Robert Hooke was involved in the solution of the riddle, and the title of his resultant contribution to the *Philosophical Transactions* convinces one immediately of the essential importance of the physiology of Respiration in a book concerned with health and the preservation of it. The title of Hooke's paper was "A Supply of Fresh Air Necessary to Life." It is a title which might head any piece of propaganda by a Public Health Officer to-day. Its implications are obvious. There at once fall, as it were, on our unsuspecting heads, whole libraries of subsequent works on Fresh Air, Foul Air, Germ-laden Air, Contaminated Air, Change of Air, Sea Voyages, the Arrest of Consumption, Ventilation, and the Importance of Deep Breathing. The carrier pigeons were indeed on this occasion released from their cage to soar into the larger air.

There were four stages in the discovery, and these four stages were due to the investigations of four great men, all members of the Oxford group, and all of them Fellows of the Royal

Society. The election of the last was somewhat delayed, though he was probably as great as any of the previous three. Even after his death the fame of John Mayow was in a curious way sunk in the waters of oblivion for a century.

The first step was due to the Honourable Robert Boyle (1627-91), the son of the Earl of Cork, who like other seventh sons had special gifts. Boyle was primarily a chemist, but he was also a great deal more than this, for he was a great and tireless investigator into most of the branches of Natural Science, and anybody who is acquainted with the great range of Boyle's writings may be said to know the whole stirring scientific world of the seventeenth century. The attention of the curious reader may especially be drawn to the two volumes of Boyle's *Usefulness of Experimental Philosophy* (1663-71), which are unfortunately rather rare, although they can be seen in most good scientific libraries, and to the admirable and most instructive bibliography of his works, with a bibliographical and critical introduction, lately published by Dr. John Farquhar Fulton, Professor of Physiology at Yale University (Oxford Bibliographical Society).

Joseph Glanvill, besides being a grave divine and Rector of Bath Abbey Church, wrote a defence of the works of the Royal Society (*Plus Ultra*, already cited), and it is of great value to be able to obtain from this book a contemporary view of Boyle. Glanvill devotes two chapters to him and his achievements. We quote the following passage as indicative of the tribute which an acute and even a partly ecclesiastical mind could pay to this great man:

> But, Sir, I think I am fallen into things of which the *Ingenious Historian* [Bishop Sprat] hath somewhere given better *accounts*, and therefore I *draw* off; though before I quite take leave of this *Head* of my Discourse, I think fit yet further to shew the *injustice* of the Reproach of having *done nothing*, as 'tis applied to the *Royal Society*, by a *single* Instance in one of their *Members*, who alone hath done enough to oblige all Mankind, and to erect an *eternal Monument* to his Memory. So that had this *great Person* lived in those days, when men *Godded* their *Benefactors*, he could not have miss'd one of the first places among their *deified Mortals*. And you will be convinc'd that this is not *vainly* said, when I have told you, I mean the *Illustrious* Mr. *Boyle*, a Person by whose proper Merits that noble Name is as much *adorned*, as by all the *splendid Titles* that it wears.

Now Boyle, in the course of his scientific experiments into the weight and pressure of the air, had discovered by the aid of the air-pump which he, with the aid of Hooke, had devised, that if a mouse or a sparrow and a lighted candle were put into a glass vessel, and the external air was withdrawn, the candle went out, and the animal died soon after. Nor could another animal live in the same air which had proved insufficient to preserve the life of the former animal. Boyle came to the conclusion that in some way breathing and combustion were an identical process.—(*Relation betwixt Flame and the Air*, 1672, pp. 109 *et seq.*)

Boyle's former laboratory assistant, Robert Hooke (1635-1703), whom we have already met in connection with the microscope, next showed that an animal could be kept alive by artificial respiration, and that by putting the mechanism of the lungs out of action, but continuing the supply of air with a bellows, the animal could be kept alive for some time. He, therefore, inferred that it was the exposure of the blood to the air, and not the movement of the lungs, that was essential to the preservation of life.

A further most important link in the argument was then forged by Richard Lower (1631–91), a physician who when a young man had worked with Wren under Willis at Oxford, and who published in 1669 a book on the Heart and the Motion and Colour of the Blood (*Tractatus de Corde. Item de Motu & Colore Sanguinis*), which, after Harvey's, is probably the most important contribution to the classic literature of the subject. Lower's mind began to work towards some solution of the problem why arterial blood should be red and venous blood dark, and now with Hooke's experiment before him he gradually formed the opinion that the blood changed colour during its course through the lungs because of its exposure to the air, and because the blood took up some of the air. The following enormously suggestive sentence, bringing us right forward to the time of John Howard and Prison Reform, occurs in Lower's account: "Were it not for this we should breathe as well in the most filthy prison as among the most delightful pastures." He remarks also: "Wherever fire can burn with ease we can breathe with ease."

There next comes on to the scene John Mayow (1645–79), a younger man than his three Oxford friends, at once a lawyer and a physician, who by the time he was twenty-five had supplied the clue to the most baffling and elusive problem of respiration, which at the same time solved that intricate problem and presented the world with a gift, the virtual discovery of oxygen, which it refused for a century till its rediscovery by Lavoisier.

Mayow published his discoveries in a book, *Tractatus Quinque*, 1674. It is among the special rarities of medical literature. He had previously published two of these tracts in 1668, and after the publication of the first volume he appears to have withdrawn himself from the world of research. Perhaps he was discouraged by a lukewarm review of his book by Oldenburg, the Secretary of the Royal Society, in the *Philosophical Transactions*. He seems to have spent the next ten years between Bath and London, practising as a physician. Unknowingly he was one of the great figures of physiology. Had he gone on he might have been among the greatest. But he died at the age of thirty-four, and his life's work had been done by the time he was twenty-five. He is almost the Keats of physiology.

Mayow by much musing on the qualities of nitre and the manner of its formation in decomposing vegetable and animal matter had come to the conclusion that there was some constituent in the air which he called "Spiritus Nitro-Æreus". He then showed by experiment and argument too elaborate to follow here that in the identical process of respiration and combustion it is not the whole air which is taken up, but only the spiritus nitro-æreus which is in the air. By reasoning exquisite, subtle, and final, he proves that it is what we now know as oxygen that is as essential to life as it is to fire, and that it is his spiritus nitro-æreus which by chemical action changes the dark venous blood to the colour of red in arterial blood.

He explains also the use of Expiration. "About expiration it is to be noted that this serves a further purpose, namely, that together with the air driven out of the lungs, the vapour of the blood agitated by the fermentation is blown away also."

About a hundred years later, Dr. Thomas Beddoes, of Bristol (the father of Thomas Lovell Beddoes, the poet), who was interested in the therapeutic use of air, expecially for consumption, came on Mayow's book, and published extracts from it. Lavoisier had named oxygen in 1775. Thus the world at last caught up with John Mayow of All Souls' College.

CHAPTER XV

THOMAS SYDENHAM, THE MASTER OF CLINICAL MEDICINE

BUT WHAT, one asks, while all these cloistered gentlemen had been making their dissections, peering through their microscopes, forming their fine theories and drawing their conclusions, writing their Latin treatises, and themselves ultimately dying of the stone, what had been happening all this time to the wretched patient languishing in English town or village? He cannot have been having a very good time of it, and perhaps the most cheering thing that can be said is that the average man is normally healthy and does not languish often or for very long at a time. Fortunately, the art of medicine throughout the ages has had to concern itself with the exception rather than with the rule.

The immediate effect upon treatment of all the physiological research which had been going on must have been negligible, and there is a kind of grim irony in the well-known story that Harvey's practice, after his discovery of the Circulation, "fell mightily". The common ills were but little aided by the high discussions at Gresham College or at Oxford. Medicine necessarily lagged far behind research, and the actual practical application of the latter was in many cases delayed till the eighteenth and nineteenth centuries.

In the seventeenth century there was a wild and wide outburst of what may be called secular superstition. This was probably one of the reactions of the Reformation. It was an age of quacks, mountebanks, astrology, alchemy, witchcraft, nostrums, and proprietary medicines. Some of these proprietary medicines are still flourishing and can be purchased to-day under the same names as they bore then.

Nor were the learned and official curators of the public health living exactly in the sunshine of enlightenment. In our chapter on Hippocrates we have spoken of the transition from superstition and conservatism to the blazing daylight of the West. But the pall of the Dark and the Middle Ages was to

PLATE LV

PALL MALL AND WESTMINSTER IN SYDENHAM'S DAYS

Thomas Sydenham (1624-89), the most important exponent of clinical medicine from the days of his master, Hippocrates, practised in King Street, Westminster from 1650 to 1650. His house in Pall Mall, where he lived from 1667 to his death in 1689, was about 200 yards east of this view by Wenceslaus Hollar, dated 1660. "Pell Mall" is the country road seen in front of the walls of St. James's Park. The latter, until it was enclosed and drained by Henry VIII in 1531, was a wet marshy held. St. James's Square now includes the site of water conduit in the foreground.

Courtesy of Dr. J. D. Comrie.

PLATE LV

PALL MALL AND WESTMINSTER IN SYDENHAM'S DAYS

Thomas Sydenham (1624–89), the most important exponent of clinical medicine from the days of his master, Hippocrates, practised in King Street, Westminster from 1656 to 1659. His house in Pall Mall, where he lived from 1667 to his death in 1689, was about 200 yards east of this view by Wenceslaus Hollar, dated 1660. "Pell Mall" is the country road seen in front of the walls of St. James's Park. The latter, until it was enclosed and drained by Henry VIII in 1531, was a wet marshy field. St. James's Square now includes the site of water conduit in the foreground.

Courtesy of Dr. J. D. Comrie.

PLATE LV

St. JAMES'S PALACE and part of the CITY of WESTMINSTER.
Taken from the N.th side of Pall Mall
As they appeared about the Year 1660.
From an Antient Drawing in the possession of John Lennard of Bromley Esq.r F.R.M. F.R.S. &A.

1. Westminster Abby. 2. Westminster Hall. 3. St. James's Palace. 4. Pell mall. 5. Carnault.

PLATE LVI

Thomæ Sydenham, M.D.

OPERA

UNIVERSA.

In quibus non solummodò Morborum Acutorum Historiæ & Curationes novâ & exquisitâ methodo diligentissimè traduntur, verùm etiam Morborum ferè omnium Chronicorum Curatio brevissima, pariter ac fidelissima in Publici commodum exhibetur.

Editio altera, priori multùm auctior, & emendatior reddita.

Huic etiam de novo accessit Index Alphabeticus summam omnium rerum, & Curationum singularum, in gratiam studiosorum, breviter complectens.

LONDINI,

Typis *R.N.* impensis *Walteri Kettilby*, ad Insigne Capitis Episcopalis in Coemeterio D. *Pauli,* 1685.

PLATE LVI

TITLE-PAGE OF THE FIRST COLLECTED EDITION OF SYDENHAM'S
WORKS, 1685

This edition was published four years before Sydenham's death. It is called Second Edition (Editio Altera) on the title-page, but no copy of an earlier edition is known, though one is said to have appeared in 1683. In this volume are collected Sydenham's sturdy and independent writings on Fevers (including agues) and Epidemics, the Small Pox, Gout, Dropsy and Hysteria.

descend, and one has indeed to be a robust enthusiast to defend or explain away the resultant soilure.

In 1618 the Royal College of Physicians published the First Edition of the London Pharmacopœia. The Second Edition appeared in 1650, and the Third in 1677. A beginning had to be made to set the materia medica in order, and any attempt was praiseworthy, but what precisely was the pharmaceutical background while Harvey was making his dissections and delivering his Lumleian Lectures and meditating his book may be gathered from a brief quotation from Dr. Fielding Garrison's *History of Medicine*:

> Among the queer remedies contained in the three London Pharmacopœias of the period were the blood, fat, bile, viscera, bones, bone-marrow, claws, teeth, hoofs, horns, sexual organs, eggs, and excreta of animals of all sorts; bee-glue, cock's-comb, cuttlefish, fur, feathers, hair, isinglass, human perspiration, saliva of a fasting man, human placenta, raw silk, spider-webs, sponge, sea-shell, cast-off snake's skin, scorpions, swallows' nests, wood-lice, and the triangular Wormian bone from the juncture of the sagittal and lambdoid sutures of the skull of an executed criminal.

We see here with what pleasant relics the new age had to grapple.

There was also a constant state of war and jealousy between physicians, surgeons, apothecaries, and barbers, and although the physicians were a close corporation of great outward honour and dignity and learning, yet the slightest familiarity with the medical literature of the period leads one to speculate on the persistent pedantry of orthodoxy, and to feel relieved that one's interest in their writings and their treatment may remain antiquarian and need never revert to a practical emergency.

There must, however, have been some good physicians, men of high sense of duty, possessed of shrewdness and common-sense, and natural kindness, who would think more of the idiosyncrasy of the patient and the merits of the case than of what Galen may have said about the subject. One remembers with affection that good man, Dr. Nathaniel Hodges, who did not flee from the City during the Plague of 1665, but remained to help the sick and dying.

It is now to the great exemplar of such good doctors that we turn when we name Thomas Sydenham (1624–89).

Sydenham is so simple, so English, and so straightforward, that at first, as we look through his books, we may miss the fact that he was great just because he was all those things at a period in the progress of medicine which needed him greatly.

He was primarily a product of Puritanism, that living acting moral force that gave birth to a great soldier in Cromwell, a great poet in Milton, a great prose-writer in Bunyan, and now a great physician in Sydenham. Let us, before speaking further of him, seize, if we can, some passage from his writings which will impress the heroic figure on our memories:

> It is my nature to think where others read; to ask less whether the world agrees with me than whether I agree with the truth; and to hold cheap the rumour and applause of the multitude. And what is it indeed? Is it any great thing for a man to do his duty as a good citizen, and to serve the public to his own private loss, and to take no glory for doing so? If I take a right measure of the matter, I am now so old that to study my own glory is to study the glory of a nonentity. What will it help me, after my death, for the eight letters which make the word SYDENHAM, to pass from mouth to mouth amongst men who can no more form an idea of what I was than I of what they will be; of men who will know none of these (then dead and gone) of the generation before them; of men who, from the inconstancy and vicissitude of all things human, will be changed in manners and changed in language!—(Dedication to his Treatise on the Gout, 1683. *Latham's translation.*)

Is there not an echo of the great stoic Emperor, Marcus Aurelius, in that? Both men were for the verities, and Sydenham here shows also that sense, so familiar to the reader of the *Meditations*, of the fleetingness of things.

Thomas Sydenham learnt his lessons in a hard school, the period of the Civil War. He was born at Wynford Eagle, in the county of Dorset, in 1624. The neighbourhood of Dorchester, and indeed much of Dorset, was strongly Parliamentarian, and Sydenham was brought up amid all the deep seriousness of the Puritans. His father was a landed gentleman, and fought when an elderly man as a captain in the army of the Parliament, and was taken prisoner. There is a deplorable story that Sydenham's mother was killed by the Royalists, but of this tragedy the details are not clear. It is also to our present purpose to note that the future physician had four brothers, who all held commissions under Cromwell. The eldest, Colonel William Sydenham, rendered great services, was a counsellor and friend of the Protector, and at the time of the Restoration was so eminent and marked a man that he was one of twenty persons named by the House of Commons to remain outside the scope of the Act of Indemnity "in all particulars not extending to life." Springing, as he did, from such stock, there could be no doubt as to the bias of the young Thomas.

In 1642 at the age of eighteen he went to Oxford, and matriculated a Fellow Commoner at Magdalen Hall. But he was soon called away, and for nearly four years was engaged in military activities with his brothers in Dorset. In 1646 he returned to Magdalen Hall, but in 1647 he transferred himself to Wadham, to which in the following year, as we have already seen, the great Dr. Wilkins was to come as Warden. Sydenham, however, did not belong to the young Royal Society group, and seems in fact to have cared not much for these things. As we now have him here in Wadham we will pause for a moment and refer to the well-known fact that he paid little attention to the contemporary preoccupation with anatomy and physiology, and preferred to use what he considered better means for the understanding and cure of his patients. It must never be forgotten that Sydenham had been a soldier, and had been brought face to face with tragedy and the necessity for decisions, and that like many people he did not see much virtue in studies and enthusiasms in which he had no share. Sydenham's was not the purely scientific mind, which rarely seems to the outside world to occupy itself with things of the most urgent or practical importance. It is with a grim smile, therefore, that we read the following sentence, written some years later, by a man who was in the very thick of the Oxford of Boyle and Wilkins and Wren. It still exists, in Sydenham's own handwriting, among the Shaftesbury papers, and is a fragment of a treatise on medicine which he and his friend John Locke had planned to write together:

> Others have more pompously and speciously prosecuted the promotion of this art by searching into the bowels of dead and living creatures, as well sound and diseased, to find out the seeds of disease destroying them, but how with little success such endeavours have been and are likely to be attended, I shall in some measure make appear.

Nor is it with any graceless intent that we recount the well-known story that when many years later the young Sir Hans Sloane came to the great physician with a letter of introduction which described the bearer as "a ripe scholar, a good botanist, a skilful anatomist," Sydenham brushed all this aside and surprised the would-be disciple with "This is all very fine, but it won't do,—Anatomy-Botany. Nonsense! Sir, I know an old woman in Covent Garden who understands botany better, and as for anatomy, my butcher can dissect a joint full as well; no, young man, all this is stuff: you must go to the bedside, it is there alone you can learn disease."

But Sydenham must always have been pretty sure of his ground, and as a corrective to these two utterances it is necessary here to quote a passage which occurs in his Treatise on Dropsy, which he published towards the end of his life, in 1683:

> Now, that there are secret passages thro' which the waters are convey'd from the cavity of the belly to the intestines is manifest; for daily experience shews that *hydragogues* carry off as much water downwards, as if it were originally contained in the intestines themselves. But as it is not easy to account for this fact, it brings into my mind an excellent passage of *Hippocrates*, who is universally esteemed the most knowing physician the world ever had. His words are these: "Some physicians and pretenders to learning, hold it impossible to understand physic, without being acquainted with the nature of the human body, in the manner of its formation; but, I am of opinion, that what philosophers and physicians have delivered concerning nature relates more to painting than to the art of medicine."
>
> But lest this admirable author should be accus'd of error, or empirics endeavour to patronize their ignorance from this passage, I freely own, that as far as I am able to judge of practice, which ought to be the test of physicians, it is absolutely necessary a physician should be well acquainted with the structure of the human body, to enable them the better to form right conceptions of the nature and causes of some diseases. For without a knowledge of the structure of the kidneys, and urinary passages, one cannot conjecture whence those symptoms arise, which proceed from a stone's being lodged in the *pelvis*, or sticking fast in the ureters. Surgeons likewise ought to understand *anatomy*, that they may more surely avoid those vessels, or parts in their operations, which cannot be hurt without destroying the patient. Neither can they reduce dislocated bones to their natural situation, without a careful examination and thorough knowledge of the position of the bones in a skeleton.
>
> Such knowledge of the human body, therefore, is so absolutely necessary, that whoever wants it will treat diseases hoodwinked. Besides, this science may be acquired without much trouble, and in a short time; for it may be sooner learnt than other more difficult matters by persons of no great acuteness, by inspecting the human body, or the bodies of some animals.—(*Swan's translation.*)

But we left Sydenham at the age of twenty-three at Wadham. He had by this time, as a result of a chance encounter with a physician on his journey to London on his way to Oxford for the second time, determined to adopt medicine as a profession, and in 1648 he was created Bachelor of Medicine by special command of the Chancellor of the University, the Earl of Pembroke. Degrees were at times given in those days to persons considered worthy of them by the command of the King or the Chancellor or by vote of Convocation. Although in Sydenham's case the Earl of Pembroke's choice was a happy one, it cannot be supposed that the recipient's medical education had been much to speak of, for Oxford then was a centre rather for enthusiastic amateurs of medical research than of actual medical education, and Sydenham's life had been too profoundly disturbed by the realities to allow of close application to study.

Later on in the same year (1648) Sydenham was appointed to a Fellowship at All Souls, and in March, 1649, he was Senior Bursar. Sydenham's Oxford career will always afford a text for curious speculations on the subject of relative values. Did it or did it not seem extraordinary to Sydenham that at All Souls he had as a contemporary for a short time a young man named Christopher Wren? He did, however, form a lasting friendship with the Honourable Robert Boyle, to whom he afterwards dedicated his first book, that on the Method of Curing Fevers (*Methodus Curandi Febres*, London, 1665), and in the dedication he refers to Boyle's having accompanied him in visits to his patients.

But now once again we are faced by one explanation of why he could not find interest or satisfaction in the little world of scientific research which surrounded him, for in 1651 he once more left Oxford to go to the aid of that cause which would not let him rest. He had been financing his younger brother, Major John Sydenham, who had died of wounds in this same year 1651 after an engagement near Stirling, and about a month before his brother's death the Senior Bursar of All Souls had received "a commission in the first regiment of militia cavalry." So he left Oxford to the virtuosos. Cromwell was in Scotland, and Sydenham himself seems in the course of his military duties to have gone beyond the Border. But the "crowning mercy" of Worcester was in the same year, soon after which, it is to be presumed, Sydenham returned to his college. In 1655 he resigned his fellowship, and was married, down at Wynford Eagle, to Mary Gee.

This brings us to the beginning of Sydenham's professional career, for it is supposed that it was about the year 1656 that he began to practise in King Street, Westminster. His family had rendered great service to the Parliamentary Party, and it may have been with some view to patients in the official world that Sydenham chose this neighbourhood.

But although ostensibly settled in practice, Sydenham appears during the next three years to have had second thoughts as to his vocation, for in 1658 he stood as candidate for Weymouth in the first Parliament of the younger Cromwell. In this he was unsuccessful, but in the following year 1659, he received from his political friends an official appointment called Comptroller of the Pipe. This had to do with the registration of Crown leases. But it was not a good time for a Parliament man to receive patronage, for the Restoration was perilously imminent. The eldest brother, Colonel William Sydenham, would be considered little better than a regicide, and for none of that family would any appointment be tenable. Whatever the physician's apprehensions were in the matter we cannot be certain, but it is almost proved that it was in the year 1659 he went to Montpellier to further his studies in medicine. Apart from the political situation, it is probable that the entirely conscientious Sydenham found his medical knowledge inadequate for practice, and he went for a short time to be a pupil of a famous Protestant physician named Barbeyrac, who although excluded on account of his religion from a professorship, had a large following of students. Barbeyrac seems to have influenced Sydenham profoundly, for John Locke, who was at Montpellier about the year 1675, and knew both men, is reported to have said "that he never knew two men more alike in opinions and character than these two physicians."

Sydenham was back in practice again by 1661, and in 1663 he received the Licentiate of the Royal College of Physicians. By the year 1667 he was living in Pall Mall, and it was from there that, when he died in 1689, he was borne to the church of St. James's, Piccadilly.

"It is my nature to think where others read," we have heard him saying. But he is rather like the Pilgrim in Bunyan's allegory, for Sydenham, too, had one book, and the book in Sydenham's knapsack was Hippocrates. Sydenham does in a remarkable way present the medical equivalent of the Puritan ideal. At the commencement of his journey he accepted the fact that "the great Hippocrates arrived at the highest pitch of physick," and to the great model of Hippocrates, he, with simple clear-eyed faith, went back in an age of unparalleled expansion in physiological research. He looked neither to the right hand nor to the left, but was so strong in himself that he reimposed the Hippocratic method on the future course of medicine. In an age of theories, mechanical and chemical, and of physiology leading men hardly knew where, the lesson of Sydenham was so absolutely salutary that his influence has lasted to this day, and wherever medicine is taught his example is followed and his name is honoured.

It is now desired to let Sydenham speak for himself, so that the reader may get some idea of the simplicity, the integrity, the *pietas* of this great Englishman. Much has been written about him, but his own words are less known than his great fame. It should be remembered, however, that he published all his books in Latin, and the present selections are taken from the good idiomatic translation by Dr. John Swan, first published in 1742 by Edward Cave at St. John's Gate, Clerkenwell. The name of Cave reminds us of the young Samuel Johnson, and to this English edition there is prefixed a brief Life of Sydenham by Johnson, reprinted from the *Gentleman's Magazine*. Before, however, commencing a series of quotations it must be stated in what special fields Sydenham cultivated the Hippocratic grain.

What Sydenham, at the end of some centuries of interminable treatises and scholastic theories, saw with clearness of mind was that the physician had, after all, to get back to the bedside, and that the recovery of the patient must be largely an affair of Nature's, aided by such steps on the part of the physician as were prompted by direct observation and his own fund of experience. He must not attempt the cure on any academic hypothesis unrelated to the individual case before him, and if a course of treatment did not at once suggest itself, the physician must have the humbleness of mind to "wait a little" till the progress of the malady showed him what had best be done. "The lustre and excellence of the art of medicine," he says, "are not so clearly seen in elegant prescriptions, as in curing diseases."

Next Sydenham regarded a disease as an ordered process of Nature, "a vigorous effort of Nature to throw off the morbific matter." He therefore set out to observe these vigorous efforts of Nature, and to write down what he saw, so that he should accumulate a body of direct evidence to be of future use to himself and to others, in much the same way as the botanists of that period, who were just then very busy at Oxford, were endeavouring to describe and give exact representations of the plants and flowers. Sydenham, in fact, remembers them, and writes:

For, is there a shorter, or indeed any other way of coming at the morbific causes we are to encounter, or of discovering the curative indications, than by a clear and distinct perception of the peculiar symptoms? Even the smallest circumstance is of use to both these purposes. For allowing that some variety happens from the constitution of particular persons, and the method of cure, yet nature notwithstanding acts in that orderly and unchangeable manner in producing distempers, that the same disease appears attended with the like symptoms in different subjects: so that those which were observed in *Socrates*, in his illness, may generally be applied to any other person, afflicted with the same disease, in the same manner as the general marks of plants justly run thro' the same plants of every kind. Thus for instance, whoever describes a violet exactly as to its colour, taste, smell, form, and other properties, will find the description agree in most particulars with all the violets in the universe.

Concurrently with this clinical bias, Sydenham was interested in epidemics and in the diseases which in those days were known as fevers, and while Pepys was keeping his Diary (1659–69) Sydenham was writing almost as exact an account, season by season, of the epidemics in London from 1661 to 1675. In the matter of epidemics and their causes Sydenham's theories were largely Hippocratic, and he cannot be blamed for not being in a position to apply to them the results of research since his day. By some irony of circumstance he was absent from London during the Great Plague, and consequently he has not left us any full account of that great epidemic for the description of which much of his life had been a preparation. His practice lay in Westminster. The Court had left London, his patients had fled the town, and now, remembering June 1665, he writes: "But when there was danger from the near approach of the *plague* to the house wherein I lived, yielding at length to the solicitations of my friends, I accompanied the vast numbers that quitted the city, and removed my family some miles distant from it. But I returned to town in so short a time, and whilst the *plague* yet raged so violently, that on account of the scarcity of abler physicians I could not avoid being called to assist the affected." But he has left no account of the dire distress of that black year as did Dr. Nathaniel Hodges and William Boghurst, an apothecary. The theories of epidemics and fevers have changed since Sydenham's time, but his faithful descriptions have a classic value as examples of exact observation, and he may be regarded as the founder of the modern science of epidemiology.

Sydenham's third great contribution to medical science lies in his vivid first-hand accounts of certain diseases. From the age of thirty he suffered from gout, and his Treatise on the Gout (*Tractatus de Podagra*, 1683) is the record of a sufferer, and reads with something of the speed of a narrative. What acute personal experience is apparent in this observation:

> The chillness and shivering abate in proportion as the pain increases, which is mild in the beginning, but grows gradually more violent every hour, and comes to its height towards evening, adapting itself to the numerous bones of the *tarsus & metatarsus*, the ligaments whereof it affects; sometimes resembling a tension or laceration of those ligaments, sometimes the gnawing of a dog, and sometimes a weight and constriction of the membranes of the parts affected, which becomes so exquisitely painful, as not to abide the weight of the cloths, nor the shaking of the room from walking briskly therein.

In Sydenham's pages are to be found new and exact descriptions of fevers, gout, scarlatina, measles, bronchopneumonia, pleuropneumonitis, dysentery, chorea, and hysteria. These have served as models for the clinician and pathologist ever since.

> " A disease, in my opinion," Sydenham begins, "how prejudicial soever its causes may be to the body, is no more than a vigorous effort of Nature to throw off the morbific matter, and thus recover the patient. . . . Now I judge that the improvement of physick depends (1) upon getting as genuine and natural a description, or history of all diseases, as can be procured, and (2) a fix'd and complete method of cure."

But the physician must approach his case with an open mind:

> In writing, therefore, a history of diseases, every philosophical hypothesis which hath prejudic'd the writer in its favour ought to be totally laid aside, and then the manifest and natural phenomena of diseases, however minute, must be noted with the utmost accuracy; imitating in this the great exactness of painters, who, in their pictures copy the smallest spots or moles in the originals. For 'tis difficult to give a detail of the errors that spring from hypotheses, whilst writers, misled by these, assign such phenomena for diseases, as never existed, but in their own brains; whereas they ought to appear clearly, if the truth of the hypothesis, which they esteem fixed and certain, were well established. Again, if any symptom properly suiting their hypothesis, does in reality belong to the disease, to be describ'd, they lay too much stress upon it, as if it were every thing they wanted, whereas, on the contrary, if it seems repugnant to their hypothesis, their manner is,

N

either to take no notice at all of it, or but barely to mention it, unless they can by means of some philosophical subtlety, adjust it thereto, and bring it in some measure to answer their end.

And on this subject of hypotheses he says:

But tho' all *hypotheses* founded on philosophical reasonings are quite useless, since no man is possess'd of intuitive knowledge, so as to be able to lay down such principles as he may immediately build upon, yet when they result from facts, and those observations only which practical and natural phenomena afford, they will remain fixed and unshaken: so that though the practice of physic, in respect of the order of writing, may seem to flow from *hypotheses*, yet if the hypotheses be solid and true, they in some measure owe their origin to practice. To exemplify this remark: I do not use chalybeates and other medicines that strengthen the blood, and forbear evacuants in *hysteric* disorders, (unless in some particular cases where I rather exhibit opiates) because I first took it for granted, that these complaints arose from the weakness of the animal spirits; but when I learnt from a constant observation of practical phenomena, that purgatives always increas'd the symptoms, and medicines of a contrary kind always quieted them, I deduced my hypothesis from this and other observations of the natural phoenomena, so as to make the philosopher in this case subservient to the empiric. Whereas to have set out with an hypothesis would have been as absurd in me, as it would be in an architect to attempt to cover a house before he had laid the foundation, which only those who build castles in the air have a privilege of doing, as they may begin at which end they please.

And again:

As to those *chronic diseases*, the history whereof I promised you to write, my thoughts are so fully turned that way, that I wish my life may be prolonged for this reason chiefly, that, by an attempt of this nature, I may be serviceable to mankind. But the experience of every day convinces me how difficult and hazardous an undertaking this is, especially for me, whose abilities are unequal to the task; for among medicinal writers, excepting *Hippocrates*, and a very few others, we meet with little to direct the mind in its enquiries into so intricate a subject; the assistance and light which authors promise, being rather false than true lights, which tend to mislead, and not to direct the mind in its researches after the genuine procedure of nature. Most of their writings are founded upon *Hypotheses*, which are the result of a luxuriant imagination; and the symptoms of diseases (wherein their true history consists) as described by them, appear to be deduc'd from the same source; and the method of cure, also, is deriv'd from the same fictitious principles, and not from real facts, and thus becomes most destructive to mankind: so full of specious reasonings is every page of the writings of such superficial men, whilst the directions of nature are overlooks.

He is never deceived by the supposition that he has discovered "a fixed and complete method of cure" for a disease, for he confesses with his fine modesty that in his first case of dropsy (he is writing twenty-seven years later), that of Mrs. Saltmarsh, of Westminster:

> Being young and unexperienced, I could not help thinking that I was possess'd of a medicine, effectual for the cure of any kind of *dropsy*: but in a few weeks I discovered my error. For being called afterwards to another woman afflicted with the *dropsy*, which succeeded an inveterate quartan, I gave this syrup and repeated it frequently, increasing the dose by degrees; but having ineffectually attempted to evacuate the waters, inasmuch as the medicine did not operate, the swelling of the belly increased, and she dismissed me; and, if my memory does not fail me, recovered by the assistance of another physician, who administer'd more efficacious remedies.

He is always insistent that the physician shall be but the assistant at Nature's mysteries, and to this purpose he cites his master, Hippocrates:

> By these steps and helps the great *Hippocrates* arrived at the highest pitch of physick, who, after laying down this solid and fixed foundation to build the art upon, has clearly delivered the symptoms of every disease, without deducing them from any hypothesis, as appears in his books concerning *diseases*, &c. He has likewise left us some rules drawn from the observance of nature's method of promoting and removing distempers; such are his *prognostics*, *aphorisms*, and other writings of this kind. Of these particulars the theory of this venerable father of physick chiefly consisted, which not being deducted from the insignificant sallies of a wanton imagination, like the dreams of distempered persons, exhibited a genuine history of the operations of nature in the diseases of mankind. Now his theory being no more than an exact description of nature, it was highly reasonable that he should aim in his practice only at relieving diseased nature by all the means he could emply; and hence, likewise, he required no more of art, than to assist nature when she languish'd, and to check her, when her efforts were too violent; and to accomplish both these ends by the steps and method whereby she endeavours to expel the disorder: for this sagacious observer found that nature alone terminates distempers, and works a cure with the assistance of a few simple medicines, and sometimes even without any medicines at all.

So he wishes, as far as possible, not to interfere with Nature, but to let her take her course, and in the following passage we hear him expounding that doctrine for which he is especially famous, the doctrine of treatment by expectation, or wait and see:

> And indeed, if I may speak my sentiments freely, I have long been of opinion, that I act the part of an honest man, and a good physician, (not only in these diseases of child-bed women, but likewise in all acute diseases, where I cannot certainly promise that the method I make choice of will perform the cure) as often as I refrain entirely from medicine, when upon visiting the patient I find him no worse to-day than he was the day before, and have reason to suppose he will be no worse to-morrow than he is to-day. Whereas, if I attempt to cure the patient by a method, which I do not yet know to be effectual, he will be endangered, both by the experiment I am going to make upon him, and the disease itself; nor will he so easily escape two dangers as one. For tho' at present there appears no manifest sign of his amendment, yet it is certain, that the nature of an acute disease is such, that it cannot always last; and besides, every day will lessen the danger, or at least, afford the physician a more favourable opportunity, of conquering the disease, than he had before.

And again, on the same subject, how refreshing is this after the futile vapourings of his forbears:

> Under so much darkness and ignorance, therefore, my chief care, as soon as any new fever arises, is to wait a little, and proceed very slowly, especially in the use of powerful remedies; in the mean time carefully observing its nature and procedure, and by what means the patient was either reliev'd or injur'd; so as soon to embrace the one, and reject the other.

For his medicines Sydenham forsook the loathsome and elaborate remedies of his time, and used simples. Even so, to the modern mind, some of his prescriptions are very long, but it is reassuring after an acquaintance with the generality of seventeenth century prescriptions, to read over one of his shorter ones. Herrick might have turned it into verse:

> Take of cowslip flowers, one handful; boil them in enough black-cherry water to leave three ounces, when strained off, to which add syrup of white poppies, half an ounce; juice of lemons, half a spoonful; mix the whole together.

Sydenham was always a close observer and recorder of what he would have called the natural history of epidemics. Of the Cholera Morbus he says very confidently, "It comes almost as constantly at the close of *summer*, and towards the beginning of *autumn*, as swallows in the beginning of *spring*, and cuckows

towards *midsummer*." He first described and indeed named
scarlet fever, and his description if it must serve as our one
example of the entire series of those classic descriptions which
have been read and re-read by generations of physicians all
over the world:

> Tho' the *scarlet fever* may happen at any time, yet it generally
> comes at the close of summer, when it seizes whole families, but
> especially children. (1) A chilness and shivering come at the
> beginning, as in other fevers, but without great sickness; (2) after-
> wards the whole skin is covered with small red spots; which are
> more numerous, larger, and redder, but not so uniform as those
> which constitute the measles; (3) they continue two or three days,
> and after they are vanish'd, and the skin is scaled off, there remains
> a kind of branny scales, dispersed over the body, which fall off,
> and come again for twice or thrice successively.
>
> As this disease seems to me to be nothing more, than a moderate
> effervescence of the blood, occasioned by the heat of the preceding
> summer, or some other way, I do nothing that may prevent the
> despumation of the blood, and the expulsion of the peccant matter
> thro' the pores, which is quickly enough perform'd. Accordingly,
> I refrain from bleeding, and the use of glysters, which make a
> revulsion, whereby I conceive the noxious particles are more
> intimately mixed with the blood, and the motion which is more
> agreeable to nature is check'd. On the other hand I forbear car-
> diacs, by the heat of which the blood may perhaps be put into
> a more violent motion, than so gentle and mild a separation as
> effects the cure requires; and besides by this means a high fever
> may be occasioned. I judge it sufficient for the patient to refrain
> wholly from flesh, and all kinds of spirituous liquors, and to keep
> his room, without lying always in bed. When the skin is entirely
> peeled off, and the symptoms vanished, 'tis proper to give a gentle
> purge, suited to the age and strength of the patient. By this plain
> and manifestly natural method, this disease in *name* only, for 'tis
> little more, is easily cured, without trouble or danger. Whereas
> on the contrary, if we add to the patient's evils, either by con-
> fining him continually in bed, or exhibiting abundance of cardiacs
> and other superfluous remedies, the disease is immediately aug-
> mented, and he frequently falls a victim to the over-officiousness
> of the physician.
>
> But it should here be observed, that when epilectic *convulsions*,
> or a COMA, arise in this disease at the beginning of the eruption,
> which sometimes happens to children and young persons; 'tis
> highly proper to apply a large and strong epispastic to the neck,
> and immediately exhibit a paregoric of *syrup of white poppies*,
> which is to be repeated every evening during the illness; and he
> must be directed to make use of milk, boiled with thrice its quantity
> of water, for his ordinary drink, and to refrain from flesh.

One of his more general descriptions must be given. What
could be more exact, more true to what most people know at

some time or other as life, than the following masterly passage on melancholia?

> But their misfortune does not only proceed from a great indisposition of body, for the *mind* is still more disordered; it being the nature of this disease to be attended with an incurable *despair;* so that they cannot bear with patience to be told that there is hopes of their recovery, easily imagining that they are liable to all the miseries that can befall mankind; and presaging the worst evils to themselves. Upon the least occasion also they indulge terror, anger, distrust, and other hateful passions; and are enemies to joy and hope; which if they accidentally arise, as they seldom do, quickly flie away, and yet disturb the mind as much as the depressing passions do, so that they observe no mean in any thing, and are only settled in inconstancy. They love the same persons extravagantly at one time, and soon after hate them without a cause; this instant they propose doing one thing, and the next change their mind, and enter upon something contrary to it, but without finishing it; so unsettled is their mind, that they are never at rest.
>
> What the *Roman* orator asserts of the superstitious, agrees exactly with these melancholic persons. *Sleep seems to be a relief from labour and inquietude, but from this many fears and cares arise;* their dreams being ever accompanied with the representation of the funerals and apparitions of their departed friends. And so much are they distempered in body and mind, that it seems as if this life were a purgatory, to expiate offences committed in a pre-existent state.
>
> Nor is this the case only in furious maniacs, but even in those, who, excepting these violent passions, are judicious persons, and for profoundness of thought, and solidity of speech greatly excel those whose minds were never disturbed by these tormenting thoughts. So that the observation of *Aristotle* is just, who asserts that *melancholy persons are the most ingenious.*

Occasionally that sense of humour which forms the basis of the amusing collection of anecdotes about Sydenham breaks out in his medical writings. He has just described his cure, by a diet of whey, of the rheumatism of Mr. Malthus, the apothecary, the ancestor of a more famous Malthus. In the last sentence he might almost be smiling at the literary felicities of Sir Thomas Browne:

> If any one should lightly esteem this method, on account of its inelegance and plainness, I must tell him, that only weak minds slight things because they are common and simple; and that I am ready to serve mankind, even at the expence of my reputation. And I must add that, were it not for the prejudice of the vulgar, I am certain that this method might be suited to other diseases, which I shall not now enumerate. And in reality it would be